Keep Faith wi

by

Hubert Snowdon

Thanks

I should like to express my thanks and appreciation to Mr. Barry Biggins
for his generous help in producing the original manuscript.

With best wishes from
Hubert H. Snowdon

Keep Faith with the Soil

by

Hubert Snowdon

Published by:
ORCHARD PUBLICATIONS
2   Orchard Close, Chudleigh, Newton Abbot, Devon TQ13 0LR
Telephone: (01626) 852714

ISBN 1 898964 44 0

Printed by:
Hedgerow Print, Crediton, Devon EX17 1ES

Dedication

To all who till the soil.

'Live always by your own unflinching toil;
Dig deep, and sow good seed; do all you can
To pay the debt you owe your country's soil
Then you need not depend on any man'.

Sa'di (1184 - 1292)

Sa'di's poem, to which I was introduced, suitably sets the theme for this book. His twelfth century sentiments and recipe for life were very similar to my own from a very young age in the twentieth century.

CONTENTS

Introduction 1

Chapter 1   Social Atmosphere 1934 2

Chapter 2   Our Farming 1934 6

Chapter 3   Farm Tradition and Attitude 11

Chapter 4   Rabbits 1934 20

Chapter 5   Young Farmers Club and Farming, 1935 26

Chapter 6   Chicken Projects 32

Chapter 7   1937 and 1938 36

Chapter 8   London 46

Chapter 9   Farm Change to War 51

Chapter 10   Girlfriends 59

Chapter 11   The Royal Marines and their Influence 66

Chapter 12   War and Farming from 1943 75

Chapter 13.   Soap 80

Chapter 14   End of the War and Conclusion 84

INTRODUCTION

This book *Keep Faith with the Soil*, is a sequel to *Born to Farm in Devon* which revealed my childhood upbringing in a typical farming family, as I believe ours to have been. It was the result of many requests to record our way of farming with horse and hand labour through the period 1918–1939.

Deemed a success the first print run sold out and a reprint undertaken. Urgent requests followed, partly because of my ageing, for this second book to record our farming into my adulthood. Which was first through peace, then war 1939–45 and return to a peace very different.

In the 1930s Britain was suffering a severe economic depression, farming was badly affected. Nevertheless leaving school in 1934 I was determined to farm.

Both farming through depression and through war was difficult. First through low prices for our unwanted produce, with farms going derelict, secondly in war every acre suddenly commanded to produce fully with fixed prices and rising costs. The weight fell on my father, who had farmed through the First World War and was a master farmer hardened to life's struggle. By his and my mother's sheer grit they were holding their own in our rented farm when others in the 1930s were going out of business.

A further struggle to be was my own. Although growing up with a good farm grounding, now as a sensitive and healthy teenager my struggle was to become a master farmer. It was not an easy matter of course, and with having a dominant parent. Because of that my father will be much mentioned.

When writing a piece on farming for a museum I kept it objective but was told there is nothing of yourself. Now writing of our own farming which is typical Devon mixed farming, I can hardly avoid being somewhat autobiographical.

The format for this second book is proposed that the story line through the years will be interspersed with a monthly diary of the usual farm work and the methods of how some farm crafts were achieved where relevant. Also, to fill in are a few attempts at rural poetry descriptive of the seasons. However thought of hereafter, it is a little indulgence on my part on the play of words and rhyme.

The diary year will commence at the second half in July because I left school that month and will follow on conveniently. Mid-summer passed into high summer when the season of growth changes to that of ripening and harvests.

Devon mixed farming demands that the farm is a busy place all year round. Milking cows of course is twice daily every day of the year. Also with their feeding and that of other livestock, some three times. Thus regular work with other odd jobs and obvious maintenance will be taken for granted and not enlarged upon unless for good reason.

CHAPTER 1
SOCIAL ATMOSPHERE 1934

I left Kingsbridge Grammar School in July 1934 having passed the Oxford School Certificate Examination with credits in mathematics and art but with a determination to join our family farm rather than further an academic career. Brought up from childhood to physical work and going on for seventeen years of age I felt that I was man and should be earning a living, not sat at a desk.

The period from 1934 to the outbreak of war in 1939 was briefly mentioned in my first book and now of interest to enlarge upon. In fact, on recall, how so much activity was seemingly crammed in can only be explained by the untiring energy of youth.

Our way of farming was typical, still with horsepower and hand labour. That was the system that I was originally asked to record, and wished to, that it shall not be forgotten.

But, first it is worth having some feeling of the social climate at the time. An atmosphere of one in the doldrums of economic depression. The original cause of which was the serious American financial crash of 1929 affecting the whole world. Here, in Britain, industrial areas were very hard hit with mass unemployment and unrest. Agriculture was depressed to its possible lowest ebb ever (except, as I write, farming is suddenly hit again, with hardly any product saleable at a profit. If there is similarity between the two, a too simple reason seems that foreign imports of food come in cheaper than we can produce them at home). The general complaint by business and workers was that there was too little money. Yet, by 1934 we were coming to terms with it. Rural areas, like our parish of Thurlestone, I feel were not too badly affected and, as others, were pulling out best they could. There was a resolve to carry on. An honesty to work for a living, taking the view – what's the use of grumbling? Possibly a left-over from the first war. Also, remembering that out parents were brought up in the energetic Victorian period.

The few, here, on the dole weren't too happy. There was the hated means test, and their money was cut by 10% in 1931 as were agricultural wages from 32/- to 31/6d per week. Old age pension was 10/- per week (50p).

Nevertheless the overall atmosphere was one generally accepted of rural areas of the time, placid, slow, unhurried living. And, no doubt, villages in beautiful scenic settings, as ours, with thatched cottages lend themselves to that famed image of tranquil English countryside.

That natural beauty was definitely ours and the few well off who found it lived the comfortable and wholesome life. There was a sense of security, our great empire and navy were still intact. I felt it myself. But for the working rest life was mostly physically demanding. We walked to work, cycled, or drove by horse and cart. This our usual mode of transport implied the slowness. Slowness was not in our work, it would not be tolerated.

My luck was to live in this small but wonderfully fertile world. Buckland Valley full of orchards, a picture flowering in spring, was my world. As a child I never wished to leave it. Hence my desire to continue farming there. A 1777 survey states that the parish had some of the finest orchards in the country. An author on rambles in the neighbourhood a century or more ago, on a first visit to West Buckland, mentioned the orchards and old world cottages to a native who replied 'Yes, it must have been built when Adam and Eve were very young!' However idyllic the landscape appears, the internal feelings of the natives cannot be seen, human complexities being what they are. They had their anxieties.

The increasing coming of the motor car brought the first signs of recovery with it, but yet made little indent into our ruralness, as it was to later. Horse transport was continuing and farming almost wholly horse-powered. Roads were little widened, narrow and rough in places. Hedges overhung with profusion of growth and wild flowers in summer. Yellowhammers and whitethroats sang on their tops, glow worms displayed at night.

The 1930s young city 'moderns' came on holiday in their bull-nosed Morris cars, or cycling and hiking singing the popular song 'I'm happy when I'm hiking'. Yet, here Victorian and Edwardian styles and beliefs persisted stubbornly with our elders, who frowned on the bare-legged new youth in shorts.

The recovery signs were the result of better working conditions, wages, and holidays with pay coming first from the cities. Our parish, near the sea, was already accommodating paying guests, including farms supplying full board, riding ponies, camping, fresh produce and special cream teas.

Further diversification was an answer, out of necessity, but was breaking and complicating traditional farming as the way of life. Money was slowly becoming more important.

JULY DIARY
Make hay while the sun shines

Mid-summer is the turning point in the year of growing to ripening. July's coming brings high summer, and the first common crop ripening is grass. Quickly running up to seed now and the sooner cut for hay the better in the longer days of drying and the better the quality.

Sheep shearing time apace.
Kingsbridge annual fair day the first Thursday after 20th July. Most important

market of the farming year and holiday for everyone wishing to attend traditional fun fair and street stalls. Trading was for all live or dead stock. Becoming special for :-

Sheep: Breeding ewes, rams, and store lambs.

Cattle: Second important advanced store cattle sale.

Merchants Annual Audit: Each merchant commandeered a hotel, pub, or suitable premises and put on a spread of food and drink, expecting farmers to settle outstanding accounts.

Countryside: Trees now in full leaf appear darker green contrasting markedly against the lighter green of recent cut hay stubbles.

Weed cut in July sure to die

Cuckoo in July away he fly.

Special Crop: Harvesting early potatoes this month. Risk missing usual first high prices if after second week in June.

METHOD

Hay Grass: cut and left in swaths by two horse machine.

Hay Turning: swaths turned up to wind and sun to aid drying by hand with hay forks, or two swath horse machine. Hay turning repeated until sufficiently dry for stacking.

Hay Raking: dried hay swaths horse raked into larger rows to aid gathering.

Hay Harvesting: Hay handpitched with forks onto waggon where a worker made the load, then carted to rick site.

Rick Building: the loose hay is pitched by hand fork from waggon to rick where it is passed to skilled rick builder who shapes the stack.

Rick Thatching: the sooner ricks thatched against rain the better.

Hay Sweeps: late 1920's hay sweeps became fashion, replacing waggons and some hand pitching. A several long toothed kind of rake loaded itself against a back rail as pulled along the rows by horse. Process was aided by horseman behind just lifting, by two handles, so rake toes dragged ground and under the hay, the unloading at rick was by lifting toes until they dug into ground and sweep somersaulted over to leave load deposited. Load was then pitched by hand on to rick or via engine driven elevators.

Hay Poles: eliminated hand pitching to rick. Hay 'grabs' lifted considerable loads at a time, hoisted up the pole and swung onto rick and released. Hoist operated by horses or machine.

Hay Balers: eventually superseded and eliminated all hand labour to machine operation.

Root Crops: last month for drilling for full crop. Drilling usually by three row horse drill.

Root Crop Hoeing: between rows by three row horse hoe set to follow drill.

Root Crop Hand Hoeing: in the rows second time, finish by end of month.

Weeds: hand pulled in corn, cut with scythe or machine in pasture.

Corn Field Hedges: better pared before corn cutting begins as hedge growth tangles into corn impeding first round of field. Resulting dried parings useful for rick bedding later.

Holding a long handled tool

Wrong, sign of weak wrists

Right, for more accuracy, both thumbs forward

Singling and hoeing crop rows.
To walk forward hoeing, the left hand is in front and the right hand is in front going back.

JULY

Wafted on winds she warmed in the Southern climes
Summer's goddess sunshine, smiling benign,
Brushes off the airiness left of Spring;
And settles fulfilling promise she brings.

As brooding hen spreads her wings protectively
She warmly nurtures 'neath her canopy.
All flora and fauna her favours shown
And with mother Nature's goodness be-stown.

We, warm-blooded, more sense environment,
Tempered, in tune with our Earth's elements.
Loaned to us are air, water, fire and soil.
More disposed are we to life's task and toil.

CHAPTER 2
OUR FARMING 1934

Our family farming at Langmans, Thurlestone, was the traditional Devon mixed farm type, with cattle, sheep, pigs and poultry and working with horses. The acreage with one or two off fields totalled about one hundred and forty, considered a medium viable holding, when surprisingly at that time the average size was only fifty acres throughout the country taking in the many smallholdings.

The land, a light loam soil, mostly faced south and sloped into the steep valley, where amidst the hamlet of West Buckland stood the farmhouse and barns. Although gratefully fertile its steepness made for a hard working farm.

Our mainstay was a dairy herd of South Devon cows supplying a parish milk round. In 1934 we obtained two shillings per gallon (3p per pint) for retailing under license to compulsory Ministry of Agriculture accredited standard. Whereas sold wholesale (for less work) to the Milk Marketing Board factory, collecting from farms since 1931, was but a few pence per gallon.

Milking cows is of course twice daily every day of the year and milk delivery by pony cart at least once a day. South Devon cattle were then reckoned dual purpose, that is giving a reasonable amount of milk, and would also fatten for beef. We reared our own calves for herd replacement and male calves for beef.

My father's usual regular staff comprised a horseman, a cowman, a maid and one or two of my sisters to help mother in the house, or outside in the yard. In summer our dairy trade increased with holidaymakers, we being near the popular Bantham Sands. Also we accommodated paying guests on full board in our seven bedroomed farmhouse. I had five sisters, one or two at home often, otherwise away in employment. Two never worked on the farm after school. Langman's kitchen was a hive of activity with dairy work, washing and scrubbing and cooking. Eight to ten ate at a large table daily.

With adequate staff I really joined the farm as odd man out, but an extra hand was always welcome in our work. My time wasn't wasted. No doubt, a son is expected to be an asset, with no wage to pay. Farmer's sons were notoriously unpaid, just keep (board) and a bob or two pocket money. We never had any money so that was no different now, and I was in the job I wanted, a fit and healthy teenager, but a very green one, who thought he was man. Any financial worries were for parents, not mine.

I could be called upon to help in the field with horse or hand labour, the milk round with Prudence our very sound cob, or after, drive her to Kingsbridge with market goods and return with purchases, or fetch cream and butter from neighbouring farms for our milk round. To work in the garden or grind grain or saw wood with our barn engine. And there were extra enterprises in the offing.

We hand milked our cows, never machine, and every member of staff had to help if required. The more of us the less cows per person, and quicker finished. The milk round was always done by a member of the family, at present a sister, driving Prudence. I continued delivering to the few houses at the top of Clanacombe hill by bicycle, as I had done going to school each morning.

My first farm job was to help re-new a post and wire fence along 'new road'. We cut the timber from Hill Top copse, horse waggoned the trunks to the farm, sawed them into posts with our barn stationary engine and circular saw, and carted them to 'new road'. We dug holes with a crow bar and Devon shovel, rammed the post in tight and re-nailed the wire. That was a job in the lull between harvests, hay-making was finished, and with August the corn harvest would be upon us. Throughout my farming career I used that possible lull for maintenance jobs, mending gates, wooden fences, stone walls.

Repairing Devon turf hedges was winter work, that is cutting off overgrown wood, re-turfing gaps and where else necessary, to about five feet in height and relaying the saplings along the top. Tenant farmers were obligated to maintain hedges in this stock proof manner, the purpose of field hedges.

Personally, this teenage man, yet to be proved, had two fitness fads. The first that I would run everywhere like African hunters and Indian tribesmen for hours on end. Not to become decadent. The second was as winter approached that I would not wear a vest. Fine for a while, but after some back-bending days in the field working until dark, and attempting to keep up with the real men, I could hardly drag my toes home walking. As the cold days came and working with father in the wind I know he was concerned watching me shivering vestless, and was putting me in shelter if possible. This was unfair to him remaining exposed. I was not as thick skinned after all.

My ageing grandfather before his death in 1933 did his best in our large walled garden. He commandeered me to help when at school and taught me sound vegetable growing. I was always happy working the soil and carried on energetically where he left off. The garden was only half cultivated, and now left to it I dug it from end to end, even transplanting the soft fruit. I wheelbarrowed loads of dung uphill to its top end. Determined, I sweated streams, and feel it running off me still. It was the only bit of farming to call my own. The result was to bring it into full production in two years, and my pride to show off in full summer growth. The produce fed family and guests and any surplus was sold on the milk round or given away.

AUGUST DIARY

If sweet Spring be king
Then June his young love
But August is Queen.

August sees the ripening of the golden corn and harvest time. The crowning of the year's endeavour of the arable field work. Always special to me as the richest farm experience. A great physical challenge in English weather to 'save' the harvest.

Late hay crop may be harvested.
Potatoes: First main crop to dig if required.
Corn stubble, 'arrish': Early harvested corn stubble may be ploughed, worked down, and drilled to catch-crops.
Special markets: Season for sales of breeding ewes, rams, and store lambs.
Fat lambs: Continue to market, finish shearing ones unsold.
Cattle: Second sales of store cattle continue.
Seasonal farmwork for bad weather: Paring hedge sides. Cutting pasture weeds with scythe or machine.

METHOD
The corn was cut and tied with cord into sheaves by the reaper-binder pulled by three horses, whereas in time gone by the whole harvest was cut by scythes. Now one use for a scythe was to cut a swath right round the edge of the field and tie it into sheaves by hand. The sheaves were stood against the hedge. This allowed the horses cutting their first round not to tread down any corn. After cutting, the field of sheaves were then stood six or eight to a stook to dry out the remaining sap, and if rained upon drained better that way. When sheaves were sufficiently dry they were waggoned to where a stack was to be built. The sheaves were first pitched from the field with forks to the waggoner, who loaded the waggon, and at the stack he pitched them off to the rick builders. In a fine season there was continuity from field to field and was a hurried sweat in hot sun often until dark, before the weather changed.
In a wet time every drying break was opportunely used to take stooks apart and face wet sides of sheaves to wind and sun. If the rain came again it was near misery stooking them up again. If the sheaves became wet in the centre each one was turned inside out by hand to dry. Sheaves stacked wet sees the grain go mouldy. By our efforts I cannot remember a field of corn or hay completely spoiled.

PARTS OF A SCYTHE

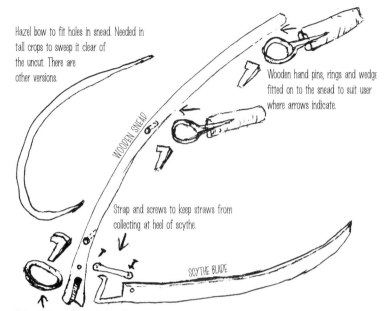

Hazel bow to fit holes in snead. Needed in tall crops to sweep it clear of the uncut. There are other versions.

WOODEN SNEAD

Wooden hand pins, rings and wedge fitted on to the snead to suit user where arrows indicate.

Strap and screws to keep straws from collecting at heel of scythe.

SCYTHE BLADE

Wedge and ring to fix tang of scythe in hole and groove cut for it.

The Scythe

The scythe superseded the sickle and was used to cut corn crops for the grain and grass crops for hay. It was also used on other crops and soft weeds such as thistles, nettles, rushes and light brambles. Tough wood stems were beyond it and have ruined many a scythe blade. It has been used for hundreds of years and despite the introduction of various cutting machines it is still employed today. Modern versions are lighter, less sturdy and 'hung' in the snead (handle) differently to the blacksmith made fittings that were preferred. These were fitted to suit the individual user on to a snead cut from the greenwood by the user.

Tools to carry:—

Sharpening stone to 'rag' scythe, requiring rough edge.

Hammer for tightening wedges.

Piece of leather to tighten behind slipping wedges

Building a stack with bouncy sheaves is a skill requiring much practice at handling that material, especially to achieve the attractive shape so often used as the symbol of British agriculture. One started to learn the art by first 'turning sheaves' on the stack, that is taking the sheaves from the waggoner turning them the way the rick builder wants them and to drop them by his side as he used them.

There were willing helpers in the village, like reserve or retired sailors having done their twenty years at Plymouth, who were brought up on farms, knew the work and its importance. Stacks that were not to be immediately threshed for the grain, would be thatched keeping them dry until wanted.

AUGUST

Glorious August breaks to blazing tune
Mature, full-bosomed more than was green June
She wears Nature's richest raiment be-gowned
In flowers and fruits, majestically crowned.

Clear blue skies and white clouds reflect the light
Displaying high summer splendidly bright.
Sun worshippers choose to revel all hours
Free on vacation from onerous chores.

They harvest a-hurry like farmers grain
Each 'ware August risks share of pouring rain.
Ill weather and wear does sully a dress
By the fading month she's in dowdiness.

Fear not the signs that summer is a 'wane
Spells of warm sunshine days return again
Through lush September to Autumnal fall
Which season brings richest colour of all.

Cuckoo in August go he must

CHAPTER 3
FARM TRADITION AND ATTITUDES

Devon mixed farming was generally standard practice from farm to farm. Understood by master and men it was adhered to almost religiously with a time and season for everything. Neighbours helping one another could fall into whatever work easily.

So much was the case, that farmers meeting at market after business and discussing the day's prices, would understand questions according to season such as – 'Did you get your swedes tilled on mid-summer day? Have you tied in your fat bullocks yet? Did you finish hoeing and cut some oats by Kingsbridge Fair Day? Who thatches the ricks on your farm?'.

Often it is suggested that farmers could economically share implements and work more with each other. Experience shows that problems arise, such as when it is your neighbours turn to help you harvest and rain is in the offing. Does he help you and next day watch his own spoiling? No. Or, if sharing implements, one uses them carefully and another doesn't, and your turn finds it very damaged, do you share the cost of repair? No! Farmers enjoy independence, and a viable farm has its own complement of implements. The responsibility their own.

The farming year divides easily into two. In summer livestock is out grazing, grass the perfect complete food. This allows time for growing and harvesting arable crops to the purpose of providing winter fodder and sell for cash. In winter when grazing ceases most of the labour is required for the feeding and management of livestock. Fortunately in dead mid-winter little arable work is possible, when livestock need is at its greatest.

Winter's end brings busy Springtime and overlaps winter feeding until May with the rush to plant crops as soon as soil conditions allow. The earlier, with proper planting, better the yield. Autumn labour reaps the different harvests, and leads into winter again.

In the 1930s, as in the past centuries, villagers brought up in the tradition willingly helped to save the harvest, knowing the importance. That is gone now with the coming of combine harvesters and grain dryers.

Farming is a necessity, we all eat, and it is a great challenge against natural hazards. Hardened men were required. There was no soft option farming for a living. I compared it with the challenge of going to sea, or underground to mine. There is an aspect of farming not commonly realised that has drawn attention more recently. I've mentioned that farmers were noted for not paying their sons. There is more reason behind that than mere meanness. Possibly stemming from days of serfdom, and now simply answered by the song 'How do you keep them down on the farm?'. One way was to keep them without money. This attitude was more prevalent than may be thought. There was always fear of losing workers and cheap family labour to more attractive industry since the Industrial Revolution.

My own father never took any interest in my Grammar School education. I know he had stated he was afraid that I may go off after school, but fair mindedly he gave me the choice. Good farmer that he was he knew that he could give me all the necessary education to farm in the tradition and doubted Kingsbridge Grammar School was needed. On some isolated farms this was seriously so. A dominant family member would keep such control that some members seldom, if ever, left the farm. They learned farming, but little else. Their only language was farm dialect, a jargon spoken only among family and to their animals.

If death or disaster struck leaving surviving 'victims' exposed to the outside world they could not cope. Though possessing intelligence they could be dubbed yokel by lack of vocabulary, compared to the higher developed speech of town dwellers who talk for a living. If yokels exist they are not only in the country.

It was recognised by the Young Farmers Club movement that many farmers did not have sufficient speech to put forward their case. They had never needed it working isolated in fields just with animals, Young Farmers Clubs introduced speech training and contests.

More recent is the case of small farmers, falsely in my opinion, considered expendable by agricultural economics, and if not voluntarily quitting their farms probably bankrupted.

The question then arose what do you do with fifty to sixty year old farmers who know nothing else? Take a man away from his culture, he or his spirit dies. If the impression given is that all dominant farmers are gaolers, that is not quite so. Any master of persons and animals has to show dominance how ever he achieves success at it. Any family with animals knows that.

When young I had great respect for several master farmers who I describe as integral men and would wish to emulate them. They appeared at all the agricultural functions, confident, hale, hearty and capable. Probably owning well run large farms handed down through family dynasties. Men with farming in their blood, reliable, regular and helpful. Important on councils, committees and dedicated towers of society.

Our family at Thurlestone were not so blessed to be wealthy and landed but from small beginnings we were offered tenancies as reliable working farmers. Although there was continued farming back in our ancestry, my father, I'm sure, believed good farming was a rightful struggle against the forces of nature. Not that he was unaware of nature, every countryman is aware. But he, with others, never championed it openly. Perhaps his Biblical belief was man's right of dominion. If a pretty flowering weed grew in his crop he hacked it out with the same vigour as a dock. I could not without a pang of wonderment for nature.

LEISURE 1934

By the 1930s village leisure had advanced from homely pleasures and local events. Every home had an accumulator powered wireless, which gave access to world wide news, verbal arts and music. But the phenomenal change was the 'talkie', cinemas with the headiness of Hollywood films at its greatest heyday portraying what we believed as American high life, romance, drama, captivating and compulsive. The unbelievable wealth and extravagance apparent carried us into a fantasy world for two hours and out of our comparative lowly drab lives.

Hired private motor cars and buses were within reach of most people to take them to the latest sumptuous town cinemas to see, mentioning a few – Fred Astaire and Ginger Rogers dance routines, Busby Berkley's spectaculars and American westerns. The grandest cinema organs reverberated their tunes during the intervals.

Some, who were able, never missed a film, seeing two weekly. Private hire cars from Thurlestone to Kingsbridge cost 5/- return for up to five persons. That was increasingly popular.

We youths cycled when free and after paying to see the film came out to fish and chips wrapped in newspaper for sixpence. We ate them walking up Fore Street where shops remained open until 9–9.30 p.m. blaring out music from deep bass radiograms. This was the excitement of the week, with news and often tunes we had just heard in the cinema. Then we cycled home often against prevailing wet weather.

In Buckland we had a men's club room, result of a rifle club formed in the first war. Here we played billiards, table tennis and cards. There were regular whist drives and occasional local concerts, great fun. Thurlestone had no football team at the time. During 1934 I played football and cricket for Kingsbridge, but my father stopped it, I left too much evening work for the rest. There were village hall dances and for ladies a W. I. flourished. An artisan golf club was attached to the main club. A weekly county council library opened.

SEPTEMBER DIARY
Month of the harvest moon

Continuation of the corn harvest is paramount in shortening days. Heavy dews and high humidity resulted in hot, sticky and tiring working conditions. Evenings, dragging home the last load with your horse and waggon under a mellow harvest moon may sound romantic, but if that moon was silvery more likely there was a nip of frost in the air. A sweaty shirt to your back turned chill and heightened your hunger. But the horses and other waiting animals always came first before our own reviving supper.

To thatch the corn ricks was essential as soon as possible. In wet sheaves grain sprouts, becomes matted together and useless. Thatching ricks was a skill to be learned and one I enjoyed, with not quite the sophistication and fine art of the house thatcher, but the same good eye and busy hands achieved the result. Rarely seen today are clumps of well built and thatched corn ricks gracing the corners of fields all over the countryside in autumn – the recognised symbol of rich abundance.

Arable work.

Stubble 'arrish' ripping first with a cultivator then harrowing to shake out the earth and burning the resulting trash is good practice. Fallen weed seed will germinate and be killed off by subsequent working.

Potatoes and early apples may be harvested.

Weed cutting and hedge paring to continue. Special sheep and cattle sales to continue.

METHOD

We made the thatching reed by threshing out the grain and combing litter from the straw of wheat sheaves. At harvest time loads of sheaves were put into a barn, convenient usually as a wet day job. In my young day there was a method of making reed by hand beating out grain and combing the litter out. One man making twelve bundles a day. That was superseded by a horse or engine driven machine, a reed-comber. That had two drums revolving in opposite directions on which were six inch spikes. A wheat sheaf was placed on a rack on the machine and held tight by a lever and the ear end pushed between the drums which beat the grain out. The sheaf was reversed and the stubble end pushed in. This removed the litter. Result was a good clean reed. A gang of four men could make up to 200 bundles in a full day. Besides our own need we supplied local house thatchers.

That method again was superseded by another form of reed comber fixed to a threshing machine. That required several men to tie bundles by hand, but today a converted straw trusser automatically ties bundles with string, several hundred a day.

The craft of thatching also included splitting spar sticks and spinning straw ropes, the means of fixing the thatch securely on the stacks. Usually hazel or willow rods were used. By a dangerous use of a small very sharp bill hook, they were split lengthwise down to size and about three feet in length, pointed sharp at each end, then 'twisted' about the centre and folded over like a hairpin. In use they

Wheat Sheaves

Sheaf bind with long straw

Sheaf bind with twisted short straw

Turning wet sheaf inside-out to dry middle

Sheaf or faggot bind with twisted hazel or willow

Stone built and thatched roof threshing barn with cut-away front to show interior.

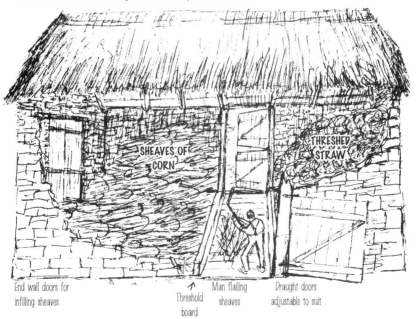

SHEAVES OF CORN

THRESHED STRAW

End wall doors for infilling sheaves

Threshold board

Man flailing sheaves

Draught doors adjustable to suit

Making thatching reed by hand from long straw wheat sheaves.

For thatching wheat is better cut slightly on the green side. Making the reeds from the sheaves is indoor labour and better left for wet days. Until such a day the sheaves are stored in a barn.

1. A sheaf is opened and a double handfull is taken and ear end is beaten over a rack to thresh out the grain.

2. Any grain remaining is flailed out on a wooden floor.

3. A handfull of reed is tied by the ears to a rope hanging from roof. The litter is hand combed off stubble end. The reed is now ready to be tied into bundles with straw binds. The binds are made long enough by tying two small handfulls of the reed together at the ear end in a reef knot.

New wheat reed is very slippery and bundles are built and tied in the following manner.
Two binds are laid on the floor and then one third of a bundle is laid across them. Another one third of a bundle is placed on top but this one protrudes about 10 inches. The final one third is placed as the first and then the binds are pulled over, twisted together and bowed under in a sheaf knot. The bundle is then stamped upright on the floor to drive the centre up as a wedge to tighten the binds. The bundle is now fit to travel.

Thatching rectangular stack with round stack behind

Straw rope spinning right hand turns, left hand feeds in straw. As rope lengthens it is hand wound on to spinner.

Splitting spars from gads of hazel or willow

Thatching.

Although slate was an often used roofing material throughout south Devon the most common was wheat reed, which was obtained by threshing out the grain from wheat straw and combing the leaf off. Houses and barns are and were thatched by specialist thatchers whilst the thatching of corn, hay and straw stacks, in order to keep the material dry and wholesome, was carried out by farmers and farm workers, skillfully, but not to the standard of house thatching. Our stacks were only thatched for the one winter and subsequently were not so thickly thatched.

Combine harvesters and balers finished the need for building and thatching stacks, although for a while some of the stacks made from the square bales of hay and straw were thatched. However, because of the water penetration and spoiling of the outside bales large asbestos barns soon appeared alongside the old stone and wooden barns to accommodate the bales of hay and straw.

The Canadian firm Allis-Chalmers produced a machine that made round bales. I bought one second-hand, the best tool I ever purchased, and the completed round bales were virtually self thatched. These were the forerunners of the much larger bales we see left for longer in the fields today. These bales are wrapped so tight the water does not penetrate so much and consequently today's farmer no longer needs to worry about the expense of building large Dutch barns.

sparred over the ropes and through the thatch then tightly pushed into the stack at suitable intervals which held the thatch in place.

Straw ropes were spun on a special tool from strands of the thatching reed of a strong good tough straw much the same as wool is spun. Fibre ropes could be purchased, we preferred to spin our own with straw. A head for heights and balance, and a proper use of a long ladder needed learning. Thatching ricks, alone, in the quiet days of autumn gave me great pleasure, relaxing a bit after the sweat of harvesting. Time to watch nature's little surprises, a fox cross the field, a pheasant to feed on the stubble, and other birds, even ducks or migrating geese dropped in for a feed and a rest. And next the boss, 'You aren't getting on fast enough!'

Through harvest or soon after, a thresh may be needed. September sees another Quarter Day: grain required for stock feed or sold for cash, bills paid and rent due. On request the contractor's steam engine and threshing machine would arrive and work to a capacity to keep ten men busy. The farmers also supplied quantities of coal and water for the engine, cider and grub for the gang. As threshed, loose straw was built into huge stacks, later thatched in with reed taken off the corn ricks.

Grain was weighed in hired sacks at two hundredweight, hand lifted on to waggons and taken to the farm barn or granary and, if required, carried in on our backs. If it was to be sold, sacks may be stacked in the field, covered with tarpaulins until the merchants collected it. Again hand lifted onto the lorries.

Drawing up foreland (voyer). Devon tenant farmers with sloping fields were obligated to draw earth that worked to the bottoms of the fields by cultivation and gravitation to the top again. About four furrows are ploughed along the bottom and by means of shovels hand loaded onto butts, carts, or by self-loading scoops and horse drawn to the top and spread. Good practice on any farm. Better done on the firm stubble, before ripping up.

The inevitable equinoctial gales setting in sometime around the end of September can upset weather and end summery spells for the year.

Drawing up foreland earth. In the county of Devon it is known as 'drawing voyer'.

On sloping arable fields soil builds up at the bottom through gravitation, cultivation and erosion. Tenant farmers were obligated to draw it up again to a higher level in the field. It is also good practice for owner occupiers.

Method:-
Four furrows were ploughed along the field bottom and
the soil shovelled on to horse drawn carts and hauled to the top of the field where it was tipped and spread by hand. Self loading scoops were introduced which were dragged as in the diagram, but this was hard work for the horses.

1. The wheel butt. A small sturdy cart with axle and two sturdy wheels at rear. The horses pulled it by a central slide and the butt was tipped and emptied by lifting one of the rear handles.

2. The butt cart with larger wheels travels easier and takes bigger loads but is higher to hand load.

3. The earth scoop self loads as horses pull it and rear handles are lifted. As it loads it balances to tip backwards in order to be dragged. It was emptied by lifting handles and tipping forward.

RUSTIC COURTSHIP

Across the harvest field strolled a fair lass
'What brought you here my beauty?' farmer asks.
'By your leave sir, because it pleased me thus,'
'Well! Tis purty you look 'mong likes of us.'

'Sir it's your honest toil I came to share.
Praise that, not just my charm at which you stare.'
'Then please pitch up some sheaves, me thinks to see
Thee in action the more pleasing will be.'

By sunset, to lass flushed and hair astray,
Farmer says, 'I've watched thee here close to-day
And mind to tell 'ee I like what I see,
To declare that I be well after thee.'

'And for what, sir, be ye well after me?'
'Truth, my dear, to learn more of what you be
And wish to find us two compatible.'
She 'My love, that I came to prove be so.'

CHAPTER 4
RABBITS 1934

Rabbits, since their introduction into Britain by the Normans have become pests. Our light farm soil suited them for easy burrowing into turf hedges where they mostly lived. Apart from digging hedges down they ate crops and where thickly populated did severe damage. They are great survivors, difficult to control. A saving grace is their edible cheap flesh, reckoned the poor man's dinner, and a usable fur skin.

When young I enjoyed a bit of rough shooting for the pot, rabbits or woodpigeons, another survivor pest. We also used ferrets and nets or farm rabbits were let cheaply to a trapper using gin traps (now illegal). That was common practice and rabbit dealers set them up with traps, then collected the catches and profitably railed them off to feed the city workers.

We reserved one or two home fields for our own use. One day my father said, 'We have too many rabbits'. True, our fields were grey instead of green, crops were weakened. We had a part-time trapper who wasn't coping. 'I'll tell him that we will catch them ourselves.' The trapper, peeved, replied, 'Say you catch three hundred, it won't pay for your time'.

The best season for rabbits as food is late autumn to early spring when they are not breeding profusely. It was autumn 1934 when I did have time. I had bought a little whippet pup, and my oldest sister exclaimed 'What a little midget', and the name Midge stuck.

Rabbit trapper staking gin trap in front of rabbit hole before covering it with sieved earth. Gin traps are now illegal.

Midge and I ferreting with nets for rabbits.

To Make a Rabbit Net

1. Take a piece of strong fine twine and tie by half hitches 16 two inch loops on to a brass ring 1–1¼ inches diameter or, cheaper, on to a loop of strong string. Next tie a stong string 2 feet to the ring and hitch it to hold tight 3 feet from the floor.

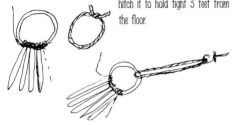

2. Fill a net needle lengthwise with strong fine twine.

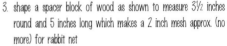

4. Now, sitting to work net, hold spacer block in left hand close to first loop of string on ring, and having tied string from needle to ring, take needle with right hand under block and up through first loop as shown. Pull it up so that edge of block is tight to bottom of loop. Pinch it here with finger and thumb.

3. shape a spacer block of wood as shown to measure 3½ inches round and 5 inches long which makes a 2 inch mesh approx. (no more) for rabbit net

5. Fling a loop to the left from the needle and take the string under and up through this loop as shown (and take in the side string for this first loop only). Pull the knot tght on the loop bottom. Do not pull it down on the single string below. Cpntinue on to second loop and so to the end of the row. Then slide the block out, turn the net over and start next row from left again. End net at the twentieth row and hand tie on to a bottom ring.

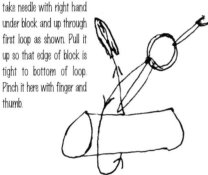

Right   Wrong

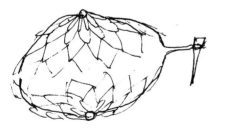

6. Net finished will catch bolting rabbits when spread over hole, but less will escape if net is pursed by threading a strong string round it and tying ends to a six inch peg which is stuck in hedge. The peg may pull out but the purse will be closed

With morning chores finished, I set off with the ferrets, nets and Midge, to the top of the farm where the hedges had little growth on top.

Nets about a yard square, bought or home made were set over all the holes either side of the hedge. Any one 'bury', that is a series of interlinking holes, must be completely netted. A ferret was put down a hole and I climbed atop the hedge where I could watch both sides. Ears and eyes are very important ferreting. Midge's were sharper than mine, I watched her head, any 'rattle' made by the chase in the bury and she pricked her ears and turned towards it. It gave me warning where a rabbit may bolt, in which event one of us quickly pounced on it. From their desperate struggles one sometimes escaped. That was Midge's use to chase and recover it. Being young she didn't always succeed, but soon hardly ever came back without her rabbit. I remember her pride in bringing her first rabbit back to me alive. Often starting seemingly too far behind, her chance came as far as two fields away, rabbits slow up near a hedge looking for a hole, that was their mistake. We killed out of necessity, not just for sport. There is way to kill a rabbit, or chicken, by breaking its neck instantly.

Every opportunity that autumn, as farm work allowed, we carried on the same. By Christmas we had caught over three hundred rabbits just on the top fields. I had not ventured down in the sheltered valley and pastures where most rabbits lie. There the hedge growth was higher and would need someone each side.

After Christmas my father came out every day possible, milk round finished, livestock tended and men put to work. We set off mid-morning and ferreted until four o'clock. That was milking time again and getting dark anyway. We averaged thirty odd rabbits a time.

We stuck at it in all weathers. Wet clothing, baggage and thirty rabbits unpaunched (un-gutted), weighing three pounds each is quite a lot to lug home. We braced the rabbits by the legs and hung them over a pole in pairs. The pole was then shouldered between us. Rabbits are best paunched when cool and on the same day as caught. We did it in the field if time allowed, otherwise a late job after milking and supper.

Some days father couldn't start with me, but came in the afternoon with Prudence in the market trap. He tied her to a hedge until we finished. What a blessing that was to ride home with our load.

One memorable afternoon in a two-and-a-half acre field, father said, 'It's getting dark, time to pack up'. There was one bury left in the corner under a bank. The nets were all set. I replied, 'Just as well try it'. We put two ferrets in and in no time at all seventeen rabbits bolted, making our total for the two-and-a-half acres ninety-nine rabbits.

There were frustrating days when ferrets 'lay up', that is, for the reasons of killing a rabbit, feeding on it well, and deciding to sleep it off, or getting trapped behind a rabbit, or deciding not to work. Once put in the hole we were at its mercy. At times they didn't reappear for hours, days, even a week. A scuffle between rabbit and ferret could be listened for and where a dog's ears are useful. If located near enough the pair could be dug out.

By the end of the season, when breeding fast again, we had caught over three thousand rabbits. I kept a strict account and estimated with those uncaught, that the farm was supporting five to six thousand, because there was little difference the following year. Then a different trapper was engaged. What they were eating, I believe, would have supported more than one hundred extra sheep. For those rabbits at 5½d each wholesale, 9d retail, we recouped only £70 to £80.

OCTOBER DIARY
Season of mists and mellow fruitfulness

If a late harvest is to be finished a St. Luke's late summer is desired.
Stubble cleaning to go apace before November rains, with burning of trash. The little trails of smoke from each heap and from different fields dotted over the countryside doing the same in company with garden bonfires was an autumn feature now unseen. Stubble burning was good practice, before chemical weed sprays, and our way of controlling weeds and diseases. It was not straw burning – a bad practice now illegal. Straw burning came with combine harvesters. Our straw was in sheaves in the stack before threshing and made use of after.

Process of corn stubble cleaning by ripping up, harrowing and burning with any weed trash present. Each working is repeated if necessary.

1. Stubble is ripped up with a tined cultivator (wheeled harrow).
2. A tined drag harrow further removes soil from stubble and weed trash.
3. Chain harrow completes process leaving stubble and trash in rolls.
4. Rolls are forked in heaps and fire carried to each.

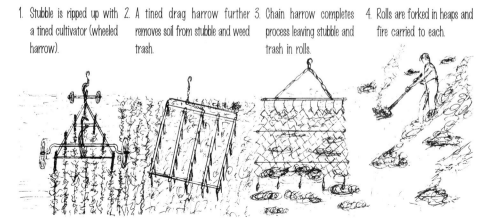

Apple harvest: Pick in cookers and desert for hoarding in store, except late ripeners. Collect windfalls into heaps to await cider making season from present time to early December. With the fruit and vegetable season advancing the farm kitchen was busy preserving for winter use.

Special shows and markets: Month of the National Dairy Show in London. Grass is growing now, as in a kind of 'second spring' and with the sun returning south is a perfect balance for dairy produce. The true spring flush is too high in protein, and with other ingredients unbalanced.

Cattle and sheep sales coming to an end in our area. Agriculture's favoured month for shows of livestock, deadstock, ploughing matches and farm craft competitions. (Now most shows are brought forward to attract holidaymakers)

Bad weather work: After rain with the soil softened turf hedging can begin as repair work. Hedge paring to continue, especially road hedges now growth is dying down. (A local bye-law put the onus on farmers to trim road hedges annually by a certain date). Hedge parings are used to cover mangel clamps to aid frostproofing. Surplus parings at this time of year to be burned were set fire on November 5th.

Season of Harvest Festivals. 'Come ye thankful people, come, all is safely gathered in'.

METHOD

Stubble ripped up with cultivator, harrowed to remove soil, and after final chain harrowing the trash is left in little rolls. These are set alight to carry fire from one to the other on a fork and keeping heaps tidied in until burnt out.

Main crop potatoes to harvest. Dug by hand with a three toed digger. Taking three rows in the field at a time, each stalk was dug separately and sorted good ware from small (scruff) and diseased. They were thrown into baskets ahead of us. If seed was to be saved, healthy egg sized tubers a third basket used. With hand picking seed, poor stalks were discarded.

AUTUMN

The languid spirit left of summer lingers still
And lurks in fields with ever lessening will.
A warm drowsiness pervades each shortening day
Reluctant to pursue the racing sun away.

Yielded of a year's abundance earth seeks rest.
Stubbles turn to brown furrows at the bright ploughs breast.
Leaf-tattered hedgerows display their ripe berried ware,
Plump fruits drop from boughs to render orchards bare.

Last grazings of pastures 'lone retain splash of green
Creepers flame a crimson hue, oak trees copper sheen.
Gold harvest grain bulges to roof from gran'ry floor,
Chirping sparrows scratch, in litter by the door.

APPLE PICKING

A ladder, a basket, a head for height,
A record hundredweight's home by night.
The weather prediction is gales next day
For apples blowing down there is no pay,

So quickly and safely, use rounded hands,
Bruising from finger-tips the boss won't stand.
The best fruit grows highest far from the ground,
Then come down picker your basket full sound.

A ladder, a basket, a head for height
It's pleasurable when weather is bright
In seasons when summer ceases to end
Even the boss seems your very best friend.
There is time to pause and savour a munch,
But watch for the worm in choice of the bunch.

CHAPTER 5
YOUNG FARMERS CLUB AND FARMING, 1935

1935 was an eventful year. My third sister Frances and I joined the newly formed Kingsbridge Young Farmers Club. Its purpose to promote agricultural education and social life with a main undertaking for members, under twenty-one, to rear calves to twelve months old and present them for an annual prize show and sale. We had missed the first year, but in May soon after the first show we drew lots for calves newly bought by the advisory committee. I was extremely lucky for three years, drawing calves with potential and took a first prize with each. The third, champion of the whole show.

The second year some members also reared gilt pigs, farrowed them and showed them with their litter. Again I won a first prize. Knowing nothing of showing pigs, the evening before I scrubbed the gilt in soapy water and bedded her and litter of nine in clean straw. Show morning I felt she lacked somehow and hit on the idea of rubbing her over with liquid paraffin. She shone brilliantly and was 'outstanding', the judge's word.

My sister Frances left the farm and younger twin sister Rosemary then reared calves for two years, winning a first and third prize. Much of our success was due to our father's knowledge of feeding and with our further attention it showed well. I was never a keen cup-hunter, but success in rearing prime livestock in competition with your fellows gives the richest experience, like corn harvest, the crowning of a year's endeavour.

Quoted, with courtesy of Kingsbridge Young Farmers Club book 'Outstanding steer among thirty animals, belonging to H. N. Snowdon of Thurlestone… was selected as champion… The best South Devon seen for a long time… opinion of the judges. One added, the best he had ever seen'.

In May King George V's twenty fifth Jubilee year was celebrated with the usual national holiday. We could never attend the early church service of thanks. It was a rush to finish the milk round and re-arrange Prudence, the market trap, and ourselves as a gypsy turn out! We won the horse class, giving us the right to lead the carnival procession from Bantham Ham through West Buckland and up to Thurlestone.

In the afternoon I excelled at the sports. Even surprisingly winning the tug-of-war with a youthful scrap team that I picked on the field because none other would challenge the heavy beer-bellied local pub team. We then dragged home to milk the cows and returned again to dance until midnight and complete exhaustion.

I was seventeen years old, father decided it was time the business needed a motor car, with me to learn to drive. A licence was purchased just before the driving test became compulsory. But a first car deal fell through because a friend, buying new offered us his old one. It was 1936 before I started lessons. I need not have passed a test but took it and passed on a second attempt in our ten horse power Clyno car.

In 1935 we grew ten acres of mangels, twice our usual amount, I don't know why. We started harvesting them early in September. I don't remember helping to pull them and strip the leaves, but our horseman and I were carting them to a clamp, when he was taken ill. My father temporarily engaged a neighbouring small holder's son who I went to school with. We took the two best cart horses and tipped to clamps the remainder. It rained incessantly, we were wet through day after day, trudging through mud in places cart axle deep.

With our normal crop there would have been altogether 450 to 500 loads. We could not keep up the average loads, up to twenty per day, in the conditions, even tipping them in the same field as grown. But we finished by mid October.

That is when I cut the tendon in my hand and my first full job that tested it after hospital and recovery was to put posts and barbed wire round the mangel clamps so that the cattle could run in the fields to eat the mangel tops left there.

Mangels if fed immediately to cattle cause stomach upsets. They need hoarding a while whilst a sugar change takes place. They hoard quicker indoors hence the tipping into special root houses, and can be fed quicker to stock needing them. The clamps outside were shaped up by hand, covered first with straw and then hedge parings for protection against the hard frosts. They were a popular crop with Devon farmers until the late 1930s. Mr. Colin Ross, Devon County Agricultural Advisor, a dour Scot, told 'As a labour intensive crop and 90% water, farmers were carrying about water'. He insisted that would be cheaper piped. Piped water to water bowls in cattle houses was not available at the time, but when introduced mangels went out of fashion.

Carting the yellow beet contrasting against the dark brown soil and green leaves on a clear, still, sunny morning was for me one of the finest rural scenes remembered. And air so still, listening, one could hear from other farms around about the bump, bump, bump, as thrown mangels hit the floor of the carts. November a bad month? Very variable and compares with March.

It is the frost which brings full colour to the late Devon autumn and is richest in November. Oak trees to bronze, elms deep yellow gold, ash a paler yellow and creepers crimson. Yet, in a wet month with no frost, they show little colour but dirty brown. In either case they are soon stripped by gales to winter bareness.

NOVEMBER DIARY
Please to remember the fifth of November

Farmers usually can and did supply a large bonfire, but winter has commenced. The rains come and lighting a sodden bonfire isn't easy.

One crop remains to be carried, mangel wurzels, they hoard better if rained on before harvesting. A popular crop in Devon as a large bulbous beet, sweet, with a high sugar content and enjoyed by all livestock. A labour intensive crop and not too frost hardy, October and November the ideal time for their harvest. Clear nights could give a white frost, insufficient to damage, and the beautiful clear sunny days that followed were a pleasure to work in, but a miserable job in the wet.

Swedes can be clamped, but are less susceptible to frost than mangels. In our mild south west they are with other root crops as likely folded in situ for stock, or carted out as required.

Potatoes undug should be finished.

The important change to winter feeding is now commencing as grazing loses quality and ceases, and additional hay and turnips are introduced. Time for forward steers to be tied in stalls for fattening. Other cattle to be winter housed will follow. Horses will lie in. Sheep remain out. Cows, a decision has to be made to lie in or out at night, then adhered to for the winter.

November, and just either side of it, was cider-making season. Apart from apples picked in for the house consumption, every opportunity was used to gather the remainder into a heap to await our call to the cider press, on one or other of two neighbouring farms. We knocked apples off trees with long poles if not fallen. The heap was bagged up and carted to the crushing floor above the press. A horse walking round turned the stone rollers into which apples were fed and crushed. The pulp dropped into a trough below. That was shovelled out on to the press, built up between layers of straw to capacity, the 'cheese'. Then the top of the press was screwed down to exert a great pressure by two men pushing a long iron bar to obtain the leverage needed. The apple juice flowed down into a trough then was dipped out to fill small 'pound' barrels through a funnel. Ten of those packed between straw fitted on a waggon and were returned to the farm cellar where they were carried on the back (awkward things) and placed on a 'tunner', a specially designed wooden funnel to fit on the large barrels. The bung was pulled from the small casks and when the large barrels were filled they were left to ferment. That finished they were bunged air tight and left to mature, six weeks at least, hardly ready for Christmas. Cider is a wonderful wine, wholesome, potent and sweet when tasted new in January, and should be treated as wine. Once air gets in, it turns acid very quickly. Devon orchards with their marvellous variety of apples

Cider Making.

1. Apples are crushed between granite stone rollers.

2. Pulp shovelled on to press between layers of straw. Press screwed down and juice runs into trough.

3. The juice is jugged out and poured into small pound barrels

4. Barrels are waggoned from press to cellar

5. The pound barrels are carried on back and tipped on to a tunner (special funnel) which is placed over large pipe casks.

6. Bung is pulled from pound barrels and when casks are filled the juice is left to ferment from its own yeast. Upon completion the cider casks are bunged airtight.

produced a top-class product. True cider needs nothing added. The juice ferments via its own yeast content.

Our farm was not suited to keeping many pigs. Usually two lop-eared white sows, which farrowed with litters about twice a year. We reared the litters on to sell at any age as suited. Always fattening one on for killing ourselves which was salted in brine. To have a sow farrow in November was the worst time for piglets, but to have a batch fattened at the end of the month caught the better Christmas trade. 'If you owe a man a grudge give him a litter of pigs in November born' or worse 'Leave him an old country cottage' – an old farmer's sayings.

METHOD

Mangels growing in rows were pulled up by hand by their leaves and the heavy bulbs shook off by a deft flick of the wrist. Both hands were used taking three rows at a time. The beet were all shaken to one side forming a row progressing up

Pulling, stripping, carting and clamping mangel wurzels

Clamped mangels need frost proofing usually with straw and hedge parings.

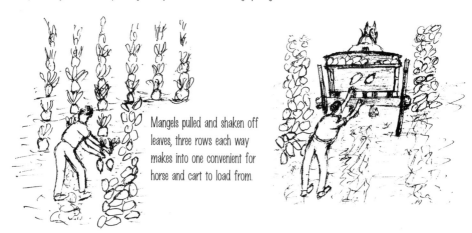

Mangels pulled and shaken off leaves, three rows each way makes into one convenient for horse and cart to load from.

the field. The next three rows running aside were pulled and shaken into the first, six in all. The next six were treated the same. The width between the resulting two rows of pulled beet was purposely made for horse and cart to drive between for loading.

'Stripping' beet by hand chaffed the forefinger and thumbs because of the rough area around the beet where dead leaves had dropped off. When wet, the leaves became slimy and stringy and difficult to handle, which needing extra shaking. Sore hands the result.

The cart was loaded throwing the beet up by hand, twelve hundredweight to a cartload and up to one ton with side boards on. They were carted to a hedge sheltered from north winds and tipped to form a large clamp. The last load each session was taken home and tipped into root-houses or near cattle sheds for early use.

ORCHARD BOY

For the boy who grows up in an orchard
From where men's cider is pressed in the main
His own vice in season, the one preferred,
Is scrunching until his stomach complains.

He recovers and looks to more scrunching
But Jack Frost has nipped the few left outdoors.
He turns to where the picked fruit are hoarding
And finds them locked away safe in store.

Through the keyhole he first spies the cookers
Tipped into heaps on the floor as they strew
They are Bramleys, Lord Derbies and Spreaders
But still green and sour the way that they grew.

Then behind he sees Pippins and Coxes
Yellow Chadders packed in straw on the shelves
Greasy Butchers all red in their boxes
And gold Russets his favourite themselves.

As he clings to the door with a longing
Pervades strongly to his keen sense of smell
The aroma of fruit all ripening
Swears he 'I'll have them, and go to hell!'

CHAPTER 6
CHICKEN PROJECTS

A business-like farmer retired from the Midlands took an interest in me. He kept a pen of Leghorn hens, known as egg machines, in his garden. He pestered me to try them offering me four dozen eggs free if I would hatch them. There was a new very cheap little incubator advertised, no more than an insulated box with a little paraffin lamp and a thermometer. I secretly bought one and set it up in my bedroom with the four dozen eggs installed. (How it didn't burn the house down was my good luck). The chicks were late, hatching irregularly after three weeks. I was anxious to get the first squeaking few out for a feed. The incubator converted into a brooder after the chicks hatched. Thirty six were placed in it. The rest of the eggs cooled and when I tested them every one had a chick. The problem was that round the edges of the incubator less heat was generated and the chicks were not quite formed. They would have all hatched in time.

Father now became interested in these healthy chicks. His feed would rear them anyway. Approaching laying time we put the pullets away from the yard hens into a new cattle shed built in the fields. When in full lay we could guarantee to pick up eggs every day for months just one or two short of their number. Perhaps it was that which persuaded father on the next project. I had no more from the first than pleasure of rearing stock.

Another value of Young farmers Clubs was exchanging of ideas, even from parents of members who met acquaintances again from their younger days. In 1936 we exchanged visits with one such family who had a parent on our advisory committee. He suggested that I would do better to buy day old chicks from a hatchery and rear them on. He was a progressive farmer and my father, who had to sanction everything, agreed we should try this. I had nothing to call my own to finance it with in any case. We bought a brooder and a hundred chicks. It was not too successful at the first attempt. Our building was too cold and there were losses to rats. But soon by designing my own brooder, rat proof and better heated, thereafter I only reckoned to lose out of each hundred just the three or four extra that came with each batch.

We separated pullets from cockerels when they were old enough to go out into rearing pens. They were cross-bred with heavy breeds that rendered both sexes fit for table birds. The pullets approaching laying were put out in field houses on fresh pasture, fifty in each. The cockerels were killed when plump at about 3–3½ pounds and before they started eating their heads off. We sold them on the milk round and any surplus sold wholesale.

It meant buying special protein high meal to augment our grain and keep up high egg production. From January I reared four or five monthly batches. It was successful farming at the time.

DECEMBER DIARY

The farm is now in full winter routine. Fodder to be carted from field to field for outlying animals and to barns for inlying stock along with bedding straw. To see the winter through to May, control of rations must be watched, increasing them towards the coldest and hungriest end.

Animals producing, such as ewes in lamb, milking cows, fattening animals and working horses need extra rations, supplied by mixtures of home grain and bought high protein cattle food. This is fed in fixed troughs in cattle sheds or portable troughs in the fields. This transporting of fodder, including waggon loads of bedding straw to barns, kept horses and staff busy. Soil conditions allowed little or no arable work except ploughing in open weather.

For hand labour at odd times hedge work and cutting wood were undertaken.

December is the month of Christmas, the greatest Christian festival celebrating the birth of Christ – traditionally for twelve days. No matter who nor where as these days approach the excitement grows and faster the preparations regardless of the extra work to normal so the enjoyment shall not be impeded.

The first Wednesday of the month is the special Kingsbridge market Christmas Fatstock Show, one of several round the district held on their own dates. It is a popular and keen competition for top honours of live and dead stock on exhibition in prime condition; world class, with our own local breeds. Dressed poultry was also of great interest this time of year. At the sale afterwards butchers enhanced their prestige by buying prize stock to kill and display in their shop with the cards awarded to winners.

One important extra could be with the sheep. Our South Devon breed will lamb early starting before and through Christmas. The value of this is that these lambs mature in twelve weeks or so and catch the good market for traditional Easter dish of spring lamb.

There was a problem with mild weather leading up to Christmas before refrigerators. Poultry to kill, pluck and dress for Christmas dinners gave us only a few days to present them before fearing they turned green. One mad rush with us up half the night. Dairy produce, especially cream and butter, was also a problem. In cold weather goods would keep for a fortnight.

The stocking up of supplies for the holiday and shopping was difficult on the farm, in that, the biggest stocking was to have all the animal requirements in place. For ourselves it was mostly home produced: vegetables, apples, preserves, pork, poultry (not turkey), eggs, dairy produce, firewood, holly, a Christmas tree, cider and ham.

Presents given were mostly from the same produce we enjoyed, few were bought. Essentials purchased were groceries, coal, imported fruit and a few luxuries. We ate rich and wholesomely, seldom alcohol except cider, with meals if required. Over indulgence spoils any party. Intoxication is not enjoyment but a poor substitute for it.

From experience I found that one week either side of the start of December produced a very cold snap often with snow showers. Then it turns milder again until Christmas or after. January will certainly produce some real winter. Dreaming of a white Christmas? Would you? With a milk round to do, horses to tend, a flock of ewes lambing in the field, a herd of cows to milk, feed, bed and muck out twice a day, a shed full of fattening bullocks, calves and pigs and poultry all to look after. Also a hired staff who want as much time off as possible. Our holiday party started after mid-day until 4 o'clock and continued from 8 o'clock until midnight. Probably far less for the womenfolk indoors. Boxing Day was easier and other parties followed until January 6th.

Those 1930's parties were the most exciting and enjoyable as any I remember with our families and teenage friends. I did describe the 1927 white Christmas in my first book.

METHOD

Hay and quality eating straw is cut from the stacks with a large knife and pitched loose on to waggons, taken to field or barn and fed to stock as required. Also roots, common green turnips first, swedes and mangels later in the season. They are loaded on to carts by hand from their field and drawn to pasture fields and thrown around for the stock. As usual another load went homeward bound for indoor stock. This diet, with the hay and straw, is sufficient for maintenance of the stock. High producing animals were fed extra protein rations.

Sheep may be folded in turnip fields, using hurdles or posts and wire netting allowing them a pen at times as required, and if possible a pasture field to run in from muddy conditions when wet.

Lean-to open linhay, with loft, adjoining threshing barn. In enclosed yard with water where young cattle are wintered to save grass fields being poached up.

Note man pushing feeding straw from loft down into rack for cattle

LOG FIRE

To what magic height does a mind aspire
Sat musing into a blazing log fire?
Watching, heat, lights, sweet scents, that burning frees
Pour from latent energy grown in trees.

Can artist's colour palette paint the hues
Of the yellows, the reds, the greens and blues;
Capture flames that leap, dart and fade away,
Black and white ash with all the shades of grey?

Could a hearth be a stage, flames the dancers,
Fiery footlights flash from white-hot embers?
Or, are the small hot caverns like suns of space
Where brave astronauts, real suns, dare to face?

What e'er thought aspires, however sane or craze
Gladsome always may Christmas Yule log blaze.

CHAPTER 7
1937 and 1938

1937 saw the coronation of George VI and the usual celebration holiday. The parish held their festivities, a church thanksgiving service, carnival, sports, tea and dancing. We won the prize for the mounted event with three boys and myself dressed as Uncle Tom Cobley and all, riding Duke our large shire. I did not do as well in the sports as in 1935, a better athlete took part.

We had a car now which we used for the milk round, marketing, farm sales, Y.F.C. activities, social trips and my winter weekly Devon County Agricultural evening classes at my old school, Kingsbridge Grammar School. A repeat of those my father attended years earlier, travelling with a neighbouring farmer. They were very helpful to us.

In the 1930s we had several mild winters and farmers were growing improved strains of French Roscoff broccoli which suited our climate and were competing with the Cornish as well. Among those farmers was the one who suggested our chicken enterprise. Now in good purpose he suggested I grew some broccoli. He offered me a thousand plants, free, that he had surplus.

Father would have to be persuaded and sought further investigation. We were efficiently equipped for our traditional farming but special crops can have special needs such as manures, protection and packing etc., as well as capital outlay.

He invited the Devon County Council horticultural advisor to walk our farm, who saw at least eight fields suitable for broccoli. Father agreed to try one acre, which we prepared to take six hundred plants.

It was usual to fence broccoli fields with rabbit proof wire. The plants we received were drying out and with time passing, against my wishes, father said, 'We'll plant first and put up the wire after'. In two nights the rabbits ate out the hearts of every one. The farmer friend displeased, kindly offered me a second lot, but father declined, I then realised he wasn't whole heartedly keen.

Incidentally the horticultural advisor noted in passing that with our light soil we were one of the few farms suited for growing English onions, for which there was good demand. But, on reflection, with that light soil which grew copious amounts of small weed all the year round in our mild climate, imagine us, before selective weed sprays, on our hands and knees hand weeding needle-like young onion shoots.

Some severe hard frost winters followed and there were losses for the broccoli growers, they now favour late April maturing curds that are less likely to damage.

Diversification also applied to changes that the motor car brought, in that we could travel faster. Therefore further in the same time for business or leisure, and in enclosed comfort. Previously the horse restricted us to its speed for our activities, keeping them local. To travel far away was a special event. Seldom seen now are men with chocked ears from chilblains, who travelled exposed in horse days. That result came about by scratching the itching sores. We were told never to scratch them. When in the spring, working the fields for corn cultivation , walking behind our horses one way with the sun on your ears, then turning round the other way with the cold breeze from the north on the same ear gave us chilblains. I never suffered them on my feet.

I was the only car driver to start with, father and two sisters learned later. I think the motor car as much as anything changed our old traditional life.

The Y.F.C. dances proved very popular to us youngsters. My parents, brought up puritanically, believed dancing wicked, father especially hated it. But he had little chance with five daughters on his hands. It was our chosen relaxation from our expected incessant work.

I also often slipped off late to popular village hall hops. Father's bedtime used to be eight o'clock and rise again, whistling, anytime after four o'clock in the morning, like the Snowdon's before him. Now with the wireless he liked to hear the 9 o'clock news before retiring, and seeing me change my clothes an hour or so earlier remarked one evening, 'What, you going out again, better you went to bed and prepared for the morning'. His whole life was his farm, little other interest outside, and very self-disciplined. He was a quiet man, didn't speak unnecessarily, but when approaching with his severe countenance set we feared what cutting remark was next. A favourite was, 'You know better than that!'. He made some of us feel so guilty. His right from wrong he cut with a knife. There were no shades of grey between, mine were many.

I enjoyed working hard on the farm especially at the jobs I liked, but grafting away at jobs I was not so keen on emphasised the need for some relief. All my young life I needed pleasure and often sought it alone, away from a family of girls and a dominant father. Then I owned that time amongst the richness of the farming I sought. More than that I possessed so little. There is human desire for possessions otherwise one feels bare and vunerable. I had enjoyed my freedom in the garden. Now with the car, and careful use of the shilling or two in my pocket, on the odd evening I could further my quest for satisfaction with a somewhat guilty feeling that it shouldn't be like this, and with uncertain outcome. Any difference with my father was in family. It didn't affect our work outside with the men, we both wanted to farm well.

SISTERS

During 1937 my third sister Frances learned to drive the car. She passed her test in the Austin Twelve-Six our second car after the Clyno's crown wheel broke. She had joined the Y.F.C. with me the previous year and reared a calf to twelve months old. Then as another diversification, with her at home, father obtained a private hire licence for the car in the popular fashion of the day, making five in West Buckland and Bantham. Possibly she asked to learn with the idea it would help her get a job, for she found a position as manageress of the Co-op dairy department in Buckfastleigh, before which she was operating the private hire business.

My oldest sister Evaline was mainstay help to mother in the house and dairy. She had done our milk round before school in the early days and helped in the farmyard. The second sister Olive after schooling took a governess post in Plymouth. She never married and throughout the war worked on telephones for the Post Office finishing up in London in a senior position.

When the twin girls after me by fifteen months left school, Margaret was apprenticed to hairdressing and Rosemary took Frances' place at home and reared calves for the Y.F.C. and for the farm. She learned to drive and also did the milk round in her turn. She enjoyed driving.

Father also eventually passed his test. So with three of us drivers as the war came we were able to cover night and day driving apart from milk round time and our own requirements. There was doubt that we could keep the taxi licence with the farm but it was permitted and the extra petrol ration to the farm allowance was useful. The beginning of the war saw an enormous movement of people. Trains were packed, standing passengers crushed to the doors. Evaline married a farmer before the war in May 1939, to live in Salcombe.

JANUARY DIARY
As the day lengthens so the cold strengthens

January, first month of a new year and the deadest, traditionally rung in by church bells. It has short days, no growth, no warmth, no dryth (drying). The ground being too wet from heavy rains, frosts and blizzards, render arable work impossible, except for ploughing in open spells. This gives more time for the extra attention that the animals need, a continuation from December, maintenance work outside and repair of hedges.

The purpose of hedges, often misunderstood today, is to keep livestock where wanted. The fact that they are now wildlife habitats is because they grew semi-naturally many wild plants, whereas the larger area they enclose, our fields, grow mono-culture crops to feed our human population and are not suited to much wildlife. It is the whole nation's population that the farmers feed. The more human population the less room for wildlife. There is a limit to the number of both that the earth can sustain healthily. If we feel responsible for both that means compromise. We all must eat to live, to fall out with farmers is to fall out with your dinner, a poor policy, especially if you grow no food.

METHOD
To turf hedges, except in hard frost!
Tools required, Devon shovel, mattock (digger), hedging bill hook and paring hook.
Pare off growth from side of hedge to be repaired, taking a length three yards or so, and note face line of original hedge. Take a digger and make a ledge not less than nine inches wide on that line as a base for first turf. First firm that ledge down ramming with back of digger. Take shovel and cut good grass faced turf from field near as possible to hedge, in brick shape. Lift turf on shovel to ledge grass outwards and so fill along first line tight together. Fill in behind turves with loose earth using shovel. Now take digger and ram whole down solid (important)

Method of repairing an overgrown Devon turf hedge to stock proof size

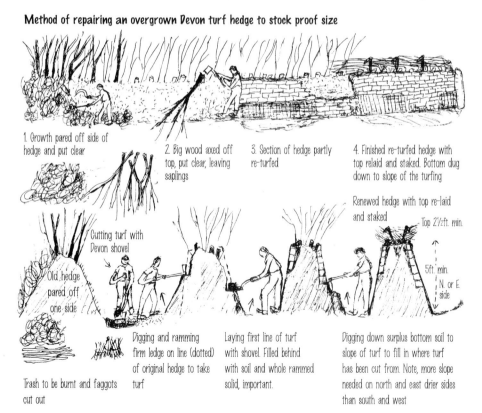

1. Growth pared off side of hedge and put clear

2. Big wood axed off top, put clear, leaving saplings

3. Section of hedge partly re-turfed

4. Finished re-turfed hedge with top relaid and staked. Bottom dug down to slope of the turfing

Renewed hedge with top re-laid and staked

Top 2½ft. min.

5ft. min.

N. or E. side

Cutting turf with Devon shovel

Old hedge pared off one side

Trash to be burnt and faggots cut out

Digging and ramming firm ledge on line (dotted) of original hedge to take turf

Laying first line of turf with shovel. Filled behind with soil and whole rammed solid, important.

Digging down surplus bottom soil to slope of turf to fill in where turf has been cut from. Note, more slope needed on north and east drier sides than south and west otherwise heavy rain can soak behind turf and work it right off keeping turf in position. Continue next layer of turf as first lot and continue to height of hedge required – five to six feet is usual. Now hedge should slope in slightly from vertical as rising to top. Finally fill in pits and level ground as well as possible.

Cutting hedge wood and relaying top.

If a hedge to be returfed has wood on top, cut off surplus wood first. To relay an overgrown hedge, using axe, saw, and billhook. Cut off overgrown wood and leave saplings for laying. Relay the saplings (after turfing if that is necessary) by cutting them almost through to an angle when they should bend over without breaking off. Sap does not like to run down, but rises to form new growth. Lay as many saplings, if available, to thickness on comb (top outer edge of hedge) that prevents animals straying. Wooden crooks or shovels of turf can hold layers in place. Animals are better kept clear by barbed wire, until hedge has grown firm and settled.

Hedge laying and other wood cutting can take place in hard frost, turfing cannot. Cut wood can be sorted, poles, firewood logs and faggots. Faggots are bundles of brushwood cut to three foot lengths and tied with a bind of hazel or willow (twisted into a loop) or string now used (bale cord).

The Devon Shovel.

The Devon shovel with its curved handle is a very versatile tool and was introduced to suit shovelling the soils and other materials of our area. The earliest shovels were shaped from wood and were a rather blunt spoon-like tool. Upon the introduction of the sharper edged metal blade it became far more efficient. The square edged common spade used by gardeners is suitable for cutting clay soils, but on soils overlying rock and generally stonier, as is often the case throughout the westcountry, a pointed tool for greater penetration is better. Persons like myself brought up to handle Devon shovels have no need of a spade or to possess one. Our tool will shovel, cut turf, spurt and turn soil, scrape, side chop, dig pits and with a longer handle fitted make the loading of various materials from the ground to vehicle loading height far easier. Another of its main purposes was to build and maintain Devon turf hedges.

The curved handles were cut from the hedgerows and woods, usually ash, willow, chestnut and hazel. So prized were these that an old saying was often heard 'Cut a shovel stick when you see it or 'twill be gone when you go back for it'. There was a preference to 'hang in' your own blade to suit yourself. The modern lighter factory made shovels are not as efficient as the old foundry made ones.

By shaping end of stick, shovel could be 'hung in' high or low to point.

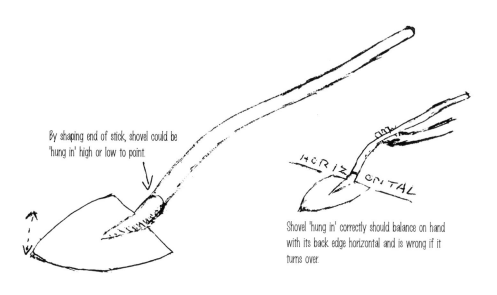

Shovel 'hung in' correctly should balance on hand with its back edge horizontal and is wrong if it turns over.

Shovelling

Spurting

Lifting

Scraping

Chopping

It is not advised to lever shovel over the knee, the easiest way to break shovel sticks.

JANUARY

Dark, drear'est month endured of the dozen all
Herdsmen must to field, feed stock and tend distress.
To face furied elements, where e're the call,
Storm, rain, blizzard, freeze, or fog's unpleasantness.

He climbs to ridge, leans to gale, scarce holding track
'Cross fields, blind from sleet, locates flock by their coughs.
Wet, mud-splodged sheep stare towards his fodder sack.
Tups stand statue-like await at feeding troughs.

He moves to sheltered hedge, cattle there behind,
Rumped, they look questionly, hungry wanting hay.
Herdsman, prepared, uncovers supply to find
Sweet dry bales sufficient rations for their day.

He leaves, head down, squints to storm churned bay.
White waves race to shore, in turn, to crash cliff high,
Shooting plumes of spray skywards in great display,
From his fields he spies each wave fragment and die.

Homeward down wan-washed pastures and over style
Hastes he 'neath bare orchard boughs to valley cot,
Quickly gathers armful from his log-wood pile
Warmed by blaze, be-chaired, forgets a while his lot.

Our parish of Thurlestone contains two land ridges with a sheltered valley between. The ridges face the sea and prevailing south west Atlantic gales and any weather that winter can throw. I have climbed both ridges many times when farming to tend stock day or night regardless.

In 1938 a surprise letter came to my father from the owner of Aune Cross House, a Mr. Creswick, who lived there with his mother. With wealth, we understood, obtained in the north of England they built their large house and two cottages for a gardener and chauffeur. The site was isolated on the hill north of Langmans. They also owned the adjoining farm of seventy acres and farmhouse in a valley beyond, named Higher Aunemouth. The land had previously been farmed by another farm owner as an off farm. The farmhouse had been occupied by an eccentric lady of independent means who bred bulldogs and treated them as children.

The letter asked if I would like to rent the farm as it had become vacant.

Obviously this chance had to be considered. For myself, I was in no position to take on a farm, but to run it in conjunction with Langmans was a possibility. My father replied that we would like to look over the farm. I had to adjust my thinking cap quickly.

I regarded Mr. Creswick as a hermit, who seemed to spend his time, with his chauffeur, tinkering with his Rolls Royce and other classic cars. Their house happened to be the last one on our milk round, Mrs. Creswick had difficulty keeping indoor staff in their isolated position and would sometimes collar me to pluck a pheasant, skin a hare, or whatever. I tried to creep in the drive silently, avoiding them. But, they were educated gentle folk, he a quiet man minded his own business and always spoke politely if we met.

I had not thought about whether the Creswicks were interested in our farming, which was of course about the only outside activity they looked upon. I knew the chauffeur, a local man, and his family were interested. They often stood watching our operations.

My father was experienced at renting farms and obtained permission for us to look over Higher Aunemouth. Farming was still in depression with many derelict farms as this one partly was. Tenanted as it had been as an off farm from an owner-occupied farm the tendency is to fatten the owned farm at the expense of the rented. Rents were comparably low, but so were farm produce prices. We had livestock, implements and labour to take it in our stride, not to underestimate the extra work.

I expected to have a farm in my own name at sometime, now all I possessed was skill and physical strength and £30 capital in a savings account. I was dependant on what my father came up with. He decided the farm was run down, in poor heart, the hedges in a bad state and was overrun with rabbits. We didn't take it on. I have since heard another experienced farmer say that he would rather pay to go into a good farm, than work up a poor one.

We did underestimate one thing, so wrapped up in our own little world we never gave thought to the small growing clouds distant on the horizon of our blue skies, caused by a little man named Adolf Hitler. We had made a big mistake, still disbelieving through the last halcyon summers of the 1930s and unseeing that in a short while from depression every agricultural acre would be needed to be in full production as war was coming with more support for farming

REFLECTIONS AND OUTCOME OF HIGHER AUNEMOUTH FARM

When we looked over Higher Aunemouth Farm I do not recall that the farmhouse was in the offer. Perhaps Mrs. Cox had not yet vacated. She was an eccentric who occupied the house and kept her bull-dogs like children. In the war if the land remained vacant it would soon be compulsorily farmed by direction of the War Agricultural Committee. The onus to farm was on the owner, Mr. Creswick in this case. He appointed Leslie his chauffeur's son as tenant. By what arrangement was not my business.

Leslie, a few years younger than me, attended the village school and finished at Sutton's good school with my sisters. He was always interested in farming and kept chickens and animals in their large garden as a boy. After which he took a partnership in a smallholding, I believe, across the River Avon on the Bigbury side. At Higher Aunemouth he set up a Guernsey milking herd, a breed he loved. He married eventually into the farmhouse and produced children there.

Before that, one day whilst passing the empty farmhouse, Mrs. Cox having vacated by now, I looked in. Finding a back entrance that opened I took the liberty to see inside. I was surprised to find a modernised four bedroom house instead of a dilapidated farmhouse.

It was too late but I thought with a little capital and a willing wife to take in paying guests, what a good start it would have been for a young farmer, even with the land in poor state. But I had none of these and it would be wishful thinking, the opportunity was not mine.

I had reason to know that Leslie was socially better adjusted especially towards the Creswicks than my aloof manner. I thought no more of it, we each carried on our own style of farming. Our two farms two valleys apart only met along the ridge road. A surprise sequel was to follow. Soon after the war finished the Creswicks died and, not having an heir, left Leslie a large fortune. I didn't envy Leslie his good luck one little bit, just thought how Mr. Creswick possibly would have helped me had I got to know him better and proved sociable towards him and taken the farm. Leslie took his family and fortune to the Channel Islands, home of his beloved cows. He died of a heart attack some years later. I wish his family well.

I recall most of the two or three years after school as the happiest and carefree a teenager should feel. The most complete awareness life can naturally achieve, as far as I know. Then it started eroding, I began to feel unhappy and couldn't understand why among the perfect surroundings I wished to live in. (I am attempting to write this as it appeared at the time, the psychology of which I understand better now). Whether influenced, or not, by the Aunemouth decision I went into 1939 with developing personal problems. My physical strength was carrying me on, but sometimes as if looking through a window at the rest of the world getting on with and enjoying life. My youth was slipping away, unachieving, were my thoughts, my trouble being a spirit needing freedom and a dominant father attempting to mould a son in his own image. The repetition of a school day's problem and me not being a 'chip off the old block'. Other astute businessmen noted my quietness, one a Y.F.C. advisor remarked 'He was one of our best, I don't know what has happened'. I was Young Farmers Chairman at the time. My year in office faded as I couldn't do it justice, and come next birthday I was over-age for office anyway.

My complaining at home only met my father's cure, 'stick it out and work harder, you'll get over it'. He was destroying my personality, unconsciously or not, the more I sought self-determination the more he opposed it. Constantly now he made me feel guilty, with nothing, near worthless, I felt tired. He remarked, 'You are tired mornings, yet fit to go off evenings'. That was so, as anyone suffering depression knows things improve as the day goes on. I still felt need of my evening escape.

TO THE DEVON VIOLET
Fragile gem of dreary winter day
Brave forerunner of the floral few
Early ones that pioneer the way.
Heralding that cheerful Spring is due.

Perfect your setting kind Nature weaves
The background cloth you appear between;
Cushion of circled overlapped leaves
Embroidered in fine shades of green.

Pendant on slim stems suspended there
You sparkle in showers, sheer delight.
Glints of purple scintillating clear
As polished crystal jewel shines bright.

But then, what costly stone can emit
A second value exquisite scent
Or, fade away when the beauty's flit
Yet re-appear fresh in one year hence.

CHAPTER 8
LONDON

To suppress anything sufficiently from the normal will produce a messy sideways outburst, as with an orange so with a human spirit. How many employees believing they are hard done by of domineering overseers turn for relief to alcohol, petty vice, or whatever and messily substitute the life they had wished?

There was nowhere for me to turn except to our family doctor. He examined me, nothing wrong physically, in fact perhaps in encouragement he said, 'Look at those fine muscles in your back.' – 'I know I have muscles, what is wrong?'. He thought a moment and replied, 'All work and no play makes Jack a dull boy. Go to London for a month!'

Of course father wasn't pleased, but I had worked just short of five years without a day off, except in 1935 when I cut a tendon in my hand and the same doctor rejoined it in hospital saying, 'Stay there a few days for shock and a rest'.

It happened that my youngest sister Margaret, the other twin, was due to take her hairdresser's diploma test at the Eugene School in Regent Street, London. Arrangements were made for us to stay with a great aunt in Wimbledon, my sister for her week, and me for a fortnight followed by a second fortnight with an in-law aunt at Highbury. I was given my fare plus £10 cash, a chicken and some apples to give to my aunt, with a similar parcel promised a fortnight later for the other relative, which I duly received. I also took my total wealth of £30 in a bank savings book. At Paddington we found trains to Wimbledon Station where we were met and carried our cases not too far distant to the house on a Saturday. My sister was due at Regent Street early Monday morning. Our aunt wisely suggested that we should find our way there on Sunday which we did taking her advised route.

We marvelled at the sights, and from Piccadilly Circus walked up Regent Street with its magnificent buildings. Quite a way up we found the Eugene School and returned to Wimbledon safely.

Our aunt warned us to be early Monday morning, but not sufficiently enough for strangers who had never experienced a London rush hour on the Underground. It found us going up the wrong staircase with hordes coming down.

We were a little late arriving at the Eugene School, a bad start for my sister. I was to leave her there and return each day at 5.00p.m. to escort her back. In the meantime I was free to see London. First I bought a good guide book, which I still have, and decided which art galleries, museums, cathedrals, were free, or cost little to enter.

I travelled on the Underground using their clear maps. Above ground I would have seen more but would never had known where I was, even when I arrived. A loner and marked visitor I didn't always get a civil answer from sharp witted Cockneys. However I achieved much seeing many treasures on view to the public, destroyed since by ravages of the coming war. I climbed to the top of St. Paul's right into the cross and signed my name there among hundreds of others, and looked out over London.

I was there during March and April 1939 and at this late date saw little preparations for war. Some obviously important buildings had windows completely sandbagged up to the first floor and at the Monument, which I also climbed, the army were recruiting showing a few armed vehicles and their new Bren gun.

At Wimbledon, after my sister had successfully returned home from her exams, I was introduced to the girl next door for younger company. A pleasant girl, a secretary and Sunday School teacher. She was learning to drive and wanted the required driver to go out with her. I had passed my test.

We made several trips over the Easter holidays, I drove her car around the recently opened Kingston By-Pass. We celebrated my twenty-first birthday simply with an old half-bottle of champagne my aunt had put aside for such an occasion and a little cake she made. I had a card from home stating that they had bought me a dart board, but would not send it up.

The girl next door took me to a London theatre show which I mentioned I would like to see. We saw Ivor Novello's 'Dancing Years' that he produced for the singer Mary Ellis. They both took part, magnificent theatre and stage scenery but the London up market protocol was too much for me, I have had more enjoyment at a village concert.

At Highbury I carried on much the same. Near Arsenal's football ground, my uncle-in-law had a season ticket, and he gave me the chance to watch them twice in their hey-day. I sat in the first reinforced concrete grandstand. What a thrill to see a top team when five forwards broke away and raced up the field passing the ball one to the other, it not touching the ground and the opposition chasing behind. Raymond Bowden, signed from Plymouth Argyle, was their centre forward.

I continued seeing the sights of London and was surprised to see so many transport horses in the streets amidst motor traffic and obeying policemen and traffic signals. We were always told the best horses left the farm to where they paid more.

Well, I had my London experience, in town feeding on tomatoes on toast and at Lyons Salad Bowl, craving salads out of season at home. Everything possible in the world could be bought in London. I made the most of it in my simple way. I enjoyed my freedom but would not live there. I returned home with some of my £30 unspent.

RETURN FROM LONDON TO WAR

I returned from London somewhat refreshed and feeling well, but as my usual apprehensive self, expecting nothing to have changed at home. After packing my suitcase away I donned my working clothes again and took my usual place at the table. Any attempt to speak excitedly or at all about the sights of London met mostly with a stony silence. My new dartboard was hung in the kitchen and we played a bit even with father joining in.

But playing at games in life was ceasing as urgent preparations for the now imminent war reluctantly speeded up. Dictates from the government and War Agricultural Office came thick and fast. On September 3rd and towards the close of that lovely long summer of 1939 with our beaches crowded with holidaymakers and sun-worshippers we listened to Prime Minister Mr. Chamberlain announce, '…consequently we are at war with Germany'. Incidentally a man drowned at Bantham beach that day.

Actually in what order the new regulations came before and after the declaration I'm not sure now, but come they did. Identity cards, gas masks, air raid precautions, warning sirens, blackouts, car headlight masks, ration books for many goods, food, clothes and petrol, seriously affected life with many more to come.

Apart from the urgent national call to arms our state of mind was changed. Largely restored from the depression, Britain's recovery allowed us to live again our pleasant way of work with time to enjoy the country we loved. The shock now put fear there. Our enemy had already proved a viscous killing machine. We were now its target, and could be killed at any time. That blight in the back of our minds goaded us to communal action and we counteracted it with great humour up front.

There were the obvious movement of troops, Reserves and the Territorial Army were immediately called up. The Local Defence Volunteers were formed, later to become the Home Guard. Air Raid Wardens appointed, and extra Special Police, Auxiliary Fire Service, plane spotters and premises were commandeered sometimes secretly for government use. The first troops in Thurlestone were the Black Watch and at Bantham 'the Buffs'.

Civilian-wise, mothers and children evacuated from cities to the country, whole schools as well, and the people who could left the cities and rented rooms at hotels and holiday cottages, the holiday trade having ceased almost completely. The village became a cosmopolitan mixture. Careless talk became criminal, giving spies information, posters appeared 'Careless Talk Costs Lives', 'Keep Mum, Like Dad'. Secrecy mattered.

Suddenly we realised how precious life was and realised our chance of survival was to all pull together, and that proved a great social leveller.

To comply with or fulfil the regulations was not always easy. From previous normality, our concentration needed raising to the importance. To blackout every chink of light from a house was not easy. (Try a window then go outside on a dark night, you will be surprised.) Often a voice from the dark shouted 'Put that light out', and the same when outside with a torch after the air raid siren had sounded, or to light a cigarette. Instructed Council Wardens coached us. Despite the seriousness it was hilarious trying out the apparatus given us, stirrup pumps, one person pumping and directing the hose at imaginary incendiary bombs, another racing with buckets of water from the nearest source. Also, the ugly gas masks and strange baby cages. We were shown how one person can rescue another unconscious person from a burning room or the like. I was the victim lying on my back. The rescuer arrives keeping low under the smoke, carrying a length of rope, or long scarf or whatever is long enough. He passes it under the victim and up under the arm pits to tie in a loop. The rescuer now kneels astride the victim and hangs loop over his own head and against his shoulders. He is now able to crawl taking with him a heavy body away from danger. I began to yell when dragged. Rescuer asked, 'What's the matter, it shouldn't hurt?' I replied, 'There are splinters from the floor sticking in my backside!'. Humour in war, plenty to keep up the moral. 'Work hard, play hard you may be dead tomorrow!' was a motto we were to live up to. A simple statement from a radio talk by an American, I think, relieved my mind, 'You aren't dead until you are killed!'. That I found quite uplifting.

Socially we were restricted to local efforts to fund a variety of war charities, groups knitting for troops, organising concerts, village hall events, sales stalls and War Savings Certificates.

We started renovating our dilapidated rifle range of the first war and with a pair of horses I hauled a hut to a high point in the parish for the Local Defence Volunteers' use at night. They also watched the sea from the cliffs when organized. We voluntarily helped one another but often being uncertain of what was required wasted our time.

Our two pubs were the only places open and were well patronised. So we entered the phoney phase of the war with the British Expeditionary Force in France and we all singing 'We'll hang out the washing on the Sigfried Line' and that silly song 'Run rabbit, run rabbit, run, run, run'.

FEBRUARY DIARY
February fill dyke
In my experience we are as likely to have snows and hard freeze ups in this month as rain. Continue stock feeding and attention.

Young sheep and cattle losing their first teeth need their turnips and mangels chopped up, unable to bite them whole. This is extra work in the fields or sheds. Ewes with early lambs may find a bite of grass greening in fields to their benefit at the end of the month.

Sometimes drying east winds allow the earliest ploughing, weathered with frost, to be harrowed twice and drilled with spring wheat or oats. Early sowing yields the best harvest, providing the soil condition is right. Hand labour continues on maintenance work and with lighter evenings showing hints of spring come the extra jobs into that busy period. Prune and plant orchard trees. Garden work, if possible, put nitrogen around spring cabbage plants or chicken manure for cabbage by Easter.

SNOWDROPS

When January's chill month comes to close,
When chinks of evening light the longer shows,
Then, yearly, a pleasant surprise we greet,
That sudden bed of snowdrops at our feet.
As white as the cold snow they oft times share.
Unseasonal for flowers! How they dare?
Stood bravely together as dense as quilt
But, each one's head bowed as if there is guilt
For choosing to bloom these favourless days.
And why the green spot that your petal displays?
Is it mote of envy for missing the fun
Of flowers that revel in full summer sun?

CHAPTER 9
FARM CHANGE TO WAR

Against the slack trade of the depression years the farm was running steadily with some little recovery and extra enterprise to aid income. Now at the outbreak of war every acre was commanded to produce as much of the basic crops as possible. A bigger turn round could hardly occur.

A War Agriculture Committee was formed comprising local experienced farmers and Ministry men. Two of whom arrived to assess our farm and decided that by the spring of 1940 we were to plough up five extra grass fields for arable crops of grain and roots, including five acres of potatoes increased from our normal two acres.

If we wished to keep our milk round, which we did, we had to take on the sale and distribution of the rationed goods known as 'fats'. That was factory butter, margarine and lard. The 'lard' was some concoction of fats to be known as 'cooking fat'. These substitutes ended the luxuries of farm made pure butter and fresh dairy cream. They became extravagances and disappeared. Customers had to register with a retailer and stick with him. We collected our supplies from a wholesaler, the butter in half-pounds, the marge and fat in bulk blocks. These had to be cut, weighed into two, three and four ounce lots, and wrapped in greaseproof according to each family's rationed allowance. This weekly irksome task made partial grocers of us. Often after a busy day on the farm we were up half the night at this task to oblige customers on the expected day of their rations. I'm sure I could cut today a half pound block of butter into exactly two ounce lots without weighing it.

Our accommodation of visitors ceased as did most holiday making except occasional home leave from the forces and other war work. Fortuitously the vacant holiday properties were needed and soon refilled by the great movement of people the start of the war caused. In our case the great aunt that I had stayed with in Wimbledon, fearfully sure that they would be bombed, begged my parents to take her and her half-brother and sister. They took over three of our rooms for the duration by some arrangement with us. Their house was bombed with a direct hit.

Our imported fruit trade ceased. Foreign fruit was rarely seen. There were children who had never seen a banana. Rose hip syrup and cod liver oil replaced it. Visitor trade lost on the milk round was balanced by the forces personnel and evacuees that took their place.

We decided to keep on the taxi service with an extra sister at home to drive. Frances lost her job as manageress of the Co-operative dairy department because rationing so reduced their dairy and meat trade to the extent that the butchery department coped with both.

Our own staff, other than myself and two sisters, were a horseman and two youths. Jobbing men were available and soon with the important realisation of food production volunteers of both sexes offered to help. Early sinking of shipping by German U-boats emphasised the need, among them H.M.S. Courageous, a Plymouth commissioned ship with loss of many local lads.

Farms were little mechanised at the time and dependant upon horse and hand labour. Our difficult farm was extravagant in hand labour to keep running efficiently.

Amidst all this change my father was suddenly taken ill, the doctor advised an immediate operation. I was called to his bedside and asked 'Could I carry on?'. In an instant I summed up the situation, but only half-heartedly replied 'I suppose so' and that because I did not know his financial position and obviously there would be business in that direction to attend to. You didn't ask parents in those days and it was never discussed, except that he always said he had no money. Apart from that worry I knew the farm work pretty well and was used to it. We had willing staff prepared to help the war effort. I did wonder from being one of them how they would accept me as the young boss. There were wages and household bills paid from milk round cash and mother took care of surplus cash, father was to sign cheques. There was the serious chance that he would not recover and if he did there would be a second operation to follow.

This was my test – whether man enough to take charge. I was twenty one years of age and should be in my prime. That spring of 1940 I had to organise the ploughing of the five extra grass fields, keep up with milk production to our milk round requirement, lamb sixty odd ewes, manage the young stock, plant the spring crops and keep the men occupied, all to the satisfaction of the War Committee. Worst of all was the business side coping with callers, reps, marketing, bargaining and having to make decisions. In this I was not experienced at all.

I knew it would be a hard challenge and I was extended to the limit. I made mistakes which didn't do my self-confidence any good, but there was no let up, and though very tired at times the challenge had to be met.

My father returned home from hospital very weak to recuperate. When I visited him he was quietly very tolerant, perhaps thankful. Now beholden he seemed trusting that I was relieving him of responsibility and carrying on his farm. I don't know what would have happened if at his bedside I had replied that I would not have carried on. I suspect he would have asked our auctioneer to sell us up and asked our landlord to relieve his tenancy. In a roundabout way I heard that a neighbouring farmer who watched my efforts, when visiting father, told him. 'Good job you have a son who can carry on so well'.

Father never praised me to my face in his whole life, it was not his style. Yet, again indirectly I know in almost a smug way he was as proud of some of my achievements as, rightly so, he was of his own farming.

From his bed he wisely advised me to approach two experienced men of his age group who I would not have considered, one to take a pair of our horses and plough our largest ley (grass) field and the other to help re-turf the hedges of the five fields before the turf was ploughed under. This was usual good practice and an obligation of our tenancy. His advice paid off to my relief. To re-turf the hedges by hand of five fields in one spring is no mean feat added to other spring work. Except for one bad hedge which we obtained permission to dig down, taking longer than I anticipated, the four of us re-turfed the rest by the end of May.

I realised that this extravagance of hand labour alone wasn't viable as in the past. Uneasily I went to my father and said, 'I'm not going to get all this work done, our horses are getting older and I don't know how to buy new ones. We must buy a tractor'.

In his weakness he broke down and cried. I believe possibly he saw it as the end of an era, which it was. He had been such a superb horseman, his pride was to breed and master fine horses. Also he knew I showed no inclination in that direction and moving into machines would be beyond his, and my, experience. He would be losing some control. However, a tractor was ordered. Meanwhile our agent loaned us an early Fordson tractor on spade lugs that had worked in the First World War. It could not do road work, but pulled up our hilly fields like a train. We got our extra crops planted and harvested. There was a six months wait before our new David Brown tractor arrived such was the unpreparedness of our country. It had rubber tyres, one of the first batch produced in England, yet I was sorry in a way to see the old Fordson go.

EARLY WAR AND DUNKIRK

The early period of war in Europe ended with Hitler's blitzkrieg attack and the ignominious retreat of the British Expeditionary Force, but with backs to the wall managed to pull off the heroic escape with the help of the little ships. As a German on television recently said, 'Their whole trapped army disappeared, we did not know where they had gone'. After that near disaster we needed a Churchill, and got him. His remarkable rallying speeches raised our spirits. Fortunately Hitler turned against Russia first, I don't believe we had the means of stopping him at that time if he had attacked Britain. Churchill was the only man I know not afraid of Hitler.

In the early days of the war our lack of preparation showed. At the call for Local Defence Volunteers, later to become the Home Guard, I went up one evening to meet outside our church. Really I hadn't the time to spare. Those gathered were put in a line to be drilled by an aged retired fisherman, who had been a sergeant in the first war. We had no arms, not even broom sticks. He, being confused as we all were, ditheringly said, 'Let me see, how did we use to form threes, or was it fours?'. After a while of this uncertainty I stepped out and said, 'I haven't the time to mess around like this, I have two shot guns at home and if the Germans arrive I hope to get one or two before they get me' and went home to work. I had felt the need to learn something of modern military defence but that uncertainty wasted our time.

As expected things on the farm did not always go well. Learning to drive a tractor on my own on our steep fields wasn't child's play. The new David Brown on rubber tyres would slip and spin on wet ground or on grass slopes. There were one or two near accidents. I consulted friends who had tractors as to how implements were hitched. We only had horse implements which were pulled behind. At times we got dug in and had to resort to horses to pull us out. That gave the old horsemen a laugh.

One problem was that horse implements were operated by the horseman walking behind where adjustment levers were placed for his convenience. Those levers could not be reached from a tractor seat. Conversions were made on some implements. With our ploughs it meant an extra man was needed to walk behind, and at a speed that he could stand all day. This annoyed me and was labour intensive. Giving it considerable thought I worked out that with just an extra chain and the plough set correctly I could pull it either way and turn around ends without getting off the tractor seat. It worked well and was faster without the

Tractor with horse plough

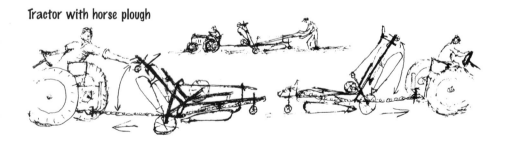

walking man and possible to plough more acreage a day than with horses. In fact a retired farmer living across the valley remarked that he had not seen ploughing like that before.

Before the David Brown arrived our yards and cattle sheds were stacked with dung of the previous winter. I didn't fancy humping that lot up our hill by horse and cart at five loads a day. I asked father if we could hire a farmer friend with his tractor and trailer to help. It was agreed and we thickly dunged a field at the top of the farm.

The farmer then suggested that he would bring his tractor plough and plough the dung in for us. I was impressed by the three furrow Lister Cockshute plough with the levers conveniently placed. Later when father was ill I bought one unbeknown to him and paid for it with part cheque he had given me for something else and some cash from the dairy. When I told him he never said a word.

The cropping did not all go well. The old pasture we ploughed was full of pests. The five acres of potatoes we planted weren't growing well. The War Agricultural Men came to check and were not pleased. Nor was I. They said the acreage was short of five. I had counted in the hedges, they paced just the crop. They came again and we dug up some of the potato tubers that we had planted. They were infested with orange wire worms sticking out like pins from a cushion. The Agricultural Men realised my position with father ill and that the failing potato crop was not my neglect. They left and I don't remember them coming back again throughout the war.

In another field the two inches high sprouting barley began to disappear.

Author with David Brown tractor, one of three later possessed.

Just to kick a toe into the soil revealed two or three leather jackets (daddy longlegs larvae) eating away at the barley roots. We poisoned them, but I had to replant the field in swedes at mid-summer which produced a heavy crop surplus to our need. The following winter I had to get someone else's sheep in to eat them. A job I could have well done without. Otherwise we grew some tremendous crops of corn and roots on those fertile fields. Thistles from the old pasture also grew well in the arable for a year or two. They were like needles in the sheaves of corn which led to complaints by the men handling them.

A forces recruiting officer turned up one day to see if any of us could be spared for call up. I genuinely could hardly spare the time to go through our work load with him. He soon summed it up and told me the same as my father was told in the first war, 'You are doing more good here than in the armed forces, troops have to be well fed'. But, he added, 'You will have to join one of the part time auxiliaries' before departing.

Fortunately the government bought all agricultural main products through a grading system for quality, and fixed prices accordingly. That eased marketing for me without bargaining and the vagaries of auctions.

I was very hard pushed at times to keep up with the seasons both to maintain required cropping and animal production. If late with the planting the final yield suffers, if animals are neglected meat and milk production suffers, which of course affected the market price on which we depended.

There was a field of wheat to be undersown with grass seeds which should have been done when the wheat was two or three inches high. It was a foot high and the ground had hardened. When harrowed the seed didn't bury and failed to grow. Better it had been left in the sack until after the wheat had been harvested, then the stubble could have been worked over and the grass seeds sown. Autumn is just as good a time for grass sowing as in spring.

We had bought new oat seed corn, a small plump grain almost like barley. I realised that it would drill more than the allotted six acres and drilled another three. That field was too late and yielded badly, better I had sown barley.

I was worried one morning that the cattle wouldn't have their ration of turnips and hay so I pushed a lad to do four cart loads, one too many. He turned up late for dinner with another man waiting to use his horse in the afternoon. We were all displeased. It was the poor horse that went without dinner that day.

When double summer time was decreed, the long days made us very tired at times. What it meant really was that we started work two hours earlier but worked on late because it was still daylight. That was fine in the spring with extra time to get the crops planted. But it was against nature in harvest time and a nuisance because the heavy dews didn't dry off the crops until mid-day. It would be afternoon before we could harvest and the sun was still shining and the harvest in full swing still at ten o'clock at night. The men didn't like it, the pubs closed at 10 p.m. and they couldn't get their deserved drink. Our cider making had also ceased through the war. Often I made a point to drive the tractor and trailer and men to reach the pub about five minutes to ten. Our landlord was very good and passed pints of beer to us over the heads of other customers if there was a queue at the bar.

My father recovered within twelve months from his operation and gradually resumed his role, seeming much like his old self.

A pair of horses were reckoned to plough one acre a day, and after ploughing one day with the new tractor plough, I was pleased to tell my father I had ploughed four acres. He coolly replied, 'Did you plough out to the hedges?' knowing that a wheeled plough cannot plough the last two furrows close to hedges. I had to admit not. 'Then you haven't finished' he said.

Some while later I happened to pass the same field again. Unknown to me he had taken three horses and with the old horse plough was ploughing there. The soil was soft and easy after a potato crop. He didn't see me watching, but he had the three horses running up the furrow and obviously was going to show me what he and horses could do. That was the spirit of the man.

I had attempted hand shearing similarly competing against machine shearing, but of course sadly we both lost out to mechanisation.

When I had finished the season with the new plough I stored it in a shed at Bantham. One evening nearing dark walking down the road I was stopped by troops on exercise. They asked 'Where was I going? What was my business?' and I was partially searched. This was the first time and was disturbing, but we became used to it through the war. Then I noticed my new plough across the road as a traffic block and further annoyed blew up explaining that it was new, cost money, and damaged could not be replaced for months impeding the war effort. They didn't care, just doing their job, and I may be a spy in disguise. I demanded to see the officer in charge. He had to be fetched from his quarters so I waited until he came and he agreed the plough should be put back. Of course the forces had many priorities of right during the war but were also held responsible for damage to civilians or their property if challenged.

MARCH DIARY

Hungry March, for livestock at their lowest point of condition. Noted for variable weather 'lamb or lion' and the cold spells as intense as ever (the great blizzard of 1891 came on 9th and 10th March). Dwindling winter fodder supplies require careful rationing. Purchased fodder if found in spring, is always expensive before grass fully arrives in May. There is a chink of green in the fields that animals crave for. Early ewes and lambs may benefit from it.

Arable work now must take any opportunity of drying weather to start cultivation and planting when soil condition is right. Early planted crops will yield best. 'A peck of dust in March is worth a king's ransom'. With livestock care and spring cultivation overlapping the spring rush has commenced.

March 29th Lady Day, a quarter day.

MAD MARCH

A shaft of sunlight pierced my room
The first to lift chill blizzard's gloom
Mad March forgot and let it in
Be gone, trickster, you cannot win
Take with you ice and winter's cold
Signs show your future's not so bold
For just beyond my window sills
I see bright yellow daffodils.
Tomorrow's April and the Spring,
Oh! Welcome mostly everything.

Mad March was written on seeing sunshine for the first time after the longest
freezing blizzard and sunless time that I remember. 1963.

PLOUGHING

Louring skies dim the winter's day
Horsemen ploughs the hill 'cross the way.
His voice breaks through the gloomy air,
Urging along his lab'ring pair.

Clean cut furrow turns 'neath ploughs beam
At steady pace of plodding team
Clinks ironwork as the shares grazed stone;
A squeaking wheel - these sounds alone
Spell out their simple message, plain,
Timely effort reaps future grain
Fresh brown earth contrasts field's grey
One acre a day earns full pay.

Apt symbol of agriculture
'God speed the plough,' prayer to assure
seed time and harvests promise clear
full barn and plenty bless each year.

Now a multi-furrowed monster
Night and day with tireless power
Turns countless hectares to what need,
Questions, will millions better feed.

CHAPTER 10
GIRLFRIENDS

From my first book *Born to Farm in Devon*, there were two humorous little criticisms. Both from friends, the first from one of my village school pals. She and her family were near good neighbours for much of our lives. I visited her on her eightieth birthday recently with a little present. Reminiscing she said, 'Don't you remember taking me to the pictures? You didn't mention that in your book'. I promised that she would be mentioned in the next. Sadly she died of a heart attack shortly afterwards and will never read it. Well Eileen, I don't particularly remember the pictures, but I do remember the birthday parties as teenagers and with your sisters and when on carol singing jaunts we all walked linking arms between distant houses singing popular songs of the day.

Secondly for Jim, a more recent friend, a retired gentleman doing immense good work as quietly as is his nature. With a twinkle in his eye he said, 'I didn't like your book, not enough sex. You mentioned one girl and then the book ended. I wanted to know how you met your wife'. Well Jim, I met a few girls before my wife to be. There were no prospects of marrying then or even through the period of this second book. That happened much later.

APRIL DIARY
Oh to be in England now that April's there

Spring Song

When late March breaks with brighter dawns
And daffodils cheer up the lawns
Then watch for migrant birds in flight
That join our songsters at first light.

When chiff-chaffs add their double note
To warbling from the blackbird's throat
With piping song and mistle thrush
Then Spring has broken Winter's hush.

When April's chorus swells each day
Then come cuckoos and birds of May.
Hear nightingales and nightjars tune
Before they fade too soon in June.

Spring arrives with warming lengthening days and kinder showers, but April is a variable month, not yet summer, and caution is the watch word. The farm grass is growing and turning livestock out to graze eases labour, but a wise farmer sees that he has sufficient winter fodder until May. An April fool can turn his stock out to graze and by the end of the month sees the fields bare of grass again after a cold spell. Some farmers prefer lambing their ewes in April for the kinder weather but those farmers who lambed early at Christmas have their lambs ready for killing now to catch the Easter trade.

As every gardener knows April is ideal for planting and a busy time. So with the farming, the warming soil dries quicker, seeds germinate quicker and the rush is on to plant as early as possible for good crops. The farm is exceptionally busy because winter feeding of stock overlaps with the spring planting until all livestock can be turned out to graze safely early in May.

The last of the corn planting is urgent and with barley, every day late planting after April 21st will result in a reduced yield – up to one hundredweight per acre per day. Hence the saying that 'May barley is no good'. But when fields of swedes or kale are still being fed to stock it's difficult to get them cleared, ploughed, and worked down for barley until late. Half a crop is better than none.

The roller comes more into use with drying soil. Earlier repeated harrowing is more useful than compacting moist soil with a roller. Turf hedging and hedge laying is still possible even with the buds shooting.

The cuckoo, in April, come he may.

The Young Farmers Club social activities and popular dances were intended to be a kind of marriage market to keep good farming stock together. Couples did meet and marry. The rest often 'put' with whom they thought, but youth seldom falls in love with whom 'put'.

At home and on other farms, there seemed to be the belief and hope that a ready made wife for a son would appear, willing to milk the cows, work indoors and out on the farm. I would be blessed! And she would work without any money too?

Then I wouldn't have needed to sow any wild oats. Well I did, and met several girls of course. Asking my father what he would do for me if I wished to marry he replied that he would furnish a cottage for me. No money was offered. That was no prospect for any girl. It was the way to keep us on the farm. We would be fed from produce of the farm. There were very few of those hardy ready made farming type who would accept those conditions. By this time most single girls were wage-earners with some spending money and expecting it. Girls I met would have genuinely made good wives but I wouldn't bring one unsuspectingly into that situation.

When driving the tractor in the fields late in 1940 I noticed a young lady regularly driving past in a small car. I learned she had come to live in Bantham and drove to a job in Kingsbridge.

A long lane ran through the middle of our farm and one day I came through a gate with a basket of eggs I had collected with our washer-lady's small boy. We met this young lady who chanced to be exploring the lane new to her. We passed the time of day and later I was told she had asked to know who was the young man she had passed.

Mentioning this little incident suggests that we would meet again. Meanwhile I came to know that her family had camped in Bantham meadows pre-war and there after rented a holiday cottage. At the outbreak of war her father rented it permanently sending mother and daughter down away from the bombing in London. Her name was Peggy Willoughby.

She hired our taxi to get to Plymouth to fetch her brother home on leave from the Merchant navy – I was to drive and she accompanied me. I was not very sociable and never spoke a word there or back, she has reminded me of this since.

The reason, was apart from my inability to converse easily with 'foreigners', I was suffering from severe nasal catarrh and infected sinuses. In my early twenties it developed into an awful irritating and debilitating condition. In my work I couldn't go near dust such as when threshing corn.

Father was disgusted, thinking I was swinging the lead and said that I should stick it through. My sleep was affected so badly on two or three occasions I went without sleep for three nights at a time. I told no-one out of the family, what was the use? I got up distressed, overtired and tried to carry on. I became diffident, a loner. That's when I made the trip to Plymouth.

A friend noticed and advised me to see a nose and throat consultant in Plymouth, who advised an operation, drilling through tissue and bone to pump the sinuses clear and hope for a cure. By chance, while I was in his waiting room I picked up a magazine – *The Psychologist*, possibly attracted by its red cover. The subject of psychology was growing popular at the time. The reading interested me to the point of ordering it regularly at home. Within a short time, as if by divine intervention, a long article on my condition appeared, the causes and cure. One of the finest health articles I have ever read. One evening I read it to the family. They sat without reply.

I asked to see a reputed psychologist in Exeter, father surprisingly approved. I was told 'You must leave home!' I had considered that many times and didn't wish to. First I would have liked more understanding at home and to work at the farming I loved. Father remarked 'Doctors aren't always right' fearing to lose my help. The pity of us two disagreeing seemed that we both needed each other, a kind of love hate relationship.

Mother had a better idea 'You need a good woman and settle down'. There was little prospect of that at the time. I took the magazine cure – change your life style to something completely different, or, if that is not possible cut out half of what you are presently doing and your health will improve. On no account have an operation on your sensitive nose.

I cancelled the Plymouth operation date and told father that I was going to stop milking cows twice a day. That was the last straw for him, our rift widened. But, I believed where you lost your shirt is where you will find it. I asked him 'You like the early morning and cows, can I do the arable and grow the crops?'. He once said to me he thought I liked growing crops rather than the animals. But he wouldn't have it, losing some control. His policy, 'Hang on to the reins as long as you can'.

But it was a cure that worked for me, my sinuses cleared up with little trouble since. Just as well it did! In 1943 father was hospitalised for his second operation and depended on me again.

That our illnesses have been dwelt on is regrettable if boring, but they were strongly remembered as landmarks that somewhat directed our lives, whereas the long spells in between, of ordinary routine work, are so easily forgotten. I would liken it to a later interest of long walks on Dartmoor, where main features are remembered and the long distances between forgotten at the expense of tired legs.

Both father and I prided our general fitness and ability in our own ways to meet the need.

LONELINESS

Laugh, they say, and the world hears,
But, the lonely cry dry inward tears.
Cry for failing at the social pace,
To fall behind is to fall from grace.

Selfish, they say, with naught to give.
No! All resources are taken to survive.
One stands self-conscious out of the pack
Look! There's cold reality staring you back.

You don't live, they say, No! One exists
Day by day, aware, and truly realist.
But you're nobody if in, a crowd you act.
Lone, one's at least an independent human fact.

Cry on! Try on friend! Try to stand
On your own, and laugh when you can.

I wrote this after I had retired from farming and like a fish out of water without it joined as many as four evening classes a week searching for a replacement interest. One class with which I produced the poem, was the local writers circle, they were great fun. But once a farmer always a farmer, perhaps a deep memory triggered it.

RABBITS AGAIN

The seriousness of the rabbit pest was not much realised outside farming until the nation's attention was aroused by the myxomatosis disease. But that came after the war.

After our 1934–35 catch of over three thousand on the farm they were becoming as bad as ever again. We were hoeing a field of swedes which in the warmth of July should be growing fast and the field looking greener every day. But the reverse was happening, more brown earth was showing every day, the young swedes eaten away by rabbits.

Father said 'Go and ask the trapper to come urgently'. The trapper, a different man from the earlier one, replied 'I'm busy but as it's urgent I'll come'. He looked around the four acre field and said to me, 'I'll need your traps as well as my own'. I had three dozen gin traps but was never very successful with them, and in July too many unwary little ones are caught while leaving the adult breeders.

He set the traps around the field in every hole. Early next morning while I was in the next field, he came up to me and said 'It's not my business to tell you, but I caught fifty rabbits last night'. He set the traps for another two or three days and just in time saved our field of swedes.

After one market day in Kingsbridge, whilst in the nearest pub we farmers were discussing rabbits when two off duty railway porters overheard us. They declared, unbelievably, that more weight of rabbits left Kingsbridge Station every week than tonnage of beef sold in the market. The weight of beef was quoted in the weekly Gazette. The porters allowed us to check their books after the last train on Saturday night when it was quiet. The nation's larder, our farms, was being seriously depleted by rabbits, such was the problem. That is why the government brought in myxomatosis, although not admitting it at first. Those people who champion dear little bunnies better feed them at their own expense in their gardens.

MAY DIARY
Cuckoo in May comes to stay

Traditionally May 1st celebrated the arrival of summer with dancing and feasting. The farm celebrates also at the relief of winter feeding of stock. The grass season has arrived when stock can be turned out to graze. But after the Lord Mayor's Show comes the dung cart. With the stock turned out cattle sheds and yards are full of a winter's accumulation of dung. This has to be carted out and spread as fertilizer. With root crops yet to be sown the best use of it is when ploughed under their seed bed.

METHOD

From the sheds dung was hand forked onto carts and horse drawn to root fields where raked off into heaps a few paces apart. These were spread and shaken evenly over the field by hand fork before being ploughed under. The ploughing was then worked down to the fine seed bed required for root crops. Mangels are better sown by third week in May. Kales and turnips by mid-summer.

Corn crops now grown to about three inches are at tillering (extra shoots sprouting at roots) stage and that is aided by rolling. Where grass seeds are to be undersown in the corn these may be broadcast and pressed into the soil by the same rolling, or by light harrowing.

Lambing is finished and if all the work is up to date there can be a pleasant spell as relaxed as any in the year.

ON SHEPHERD'S DOWN

Summer bloomed truly that Sunday in May
Beckoned that we climb the hill 'cross the way.
Three were my sisters, me boy making four
And Rosa came too, our friend from next door.

The girls wore muslin, with bright ribbons through
Me a tusser shirt and velvet shorts, blue
Higher we climbed one fore t'other with glee
Only as children are able, so free.

At the top bloomed hawthorns white as wild sea
Golden gorse, and pink flowered crab apple tree.
Finding a clearing we romped in our play
Bent on enjoying the balm of the day.

Lying in grasses we gazed at the sky
Guessing in wonderment, how wide and high?
Petals were falling a constant shower
Never there was such enchanted bower.

Suddenly, as if fate the moment chose
Rosa and I were alone and so close.
Lost to the world, we kissed, a new found heav'n.
She was just six then, and me barely seven.

CHAPTER 11
THE ROYAL MARINES AND THEIR INFLUENCE

During 1941 a Royal Marine Officer Cadet Training Unit commandeered the Thurlestone Hotel displacing a girl's school evacuated there.

The respected Royal Marines attracted much attention in the parish, over three hundred of them eventually. Their families and followers took over all the available accommodation outside the hotel extending further the already expanding population that the war brought. Their influence imposed itself upon our small village.

Much of the Royal Marine's severe and tough training was witnessed by all. They had assumed the right to exercise the cadets anywhere day or night, and to the war cause were seldom opposed. In return they allowed the public to their film shows on Monday nights and to the occasional dances and concerts in their ballroom. Their attitude was polite and jauntily proud. There was no doubt that the uniforms attracted the girls.

Before fully manned they challenged the village to a football match. We played twice winning one each. With great interest a vital final was to be played on Easter Monday. The village team won, the Royal Marines' pride was shaken, but later when at full strength of some three hundred and fifty with choice footballers amongst them they beat us handsomely.

After games we resorted to the Thurlestone Hotel public bar, now the Village Inn. Some of us became friendly with the sergeants and were invited to their mess at times. They in their free time willingly came and helped us harvest on the farm, glad to be away from the military for a while. We made friendships with their families which we still maintain.

Our farm had two evacuee schoolboys billeted on us from the Elephant and Castle area, true cockneys. One we didn't get on with and he went elsewhere. The other, a good spirited lad of nine years, stayed with us for five years. He willingly ran small errands for us and was very useful. From living seemingly on fish and chips and visits to the Trocadero Cinema he took to Devon life fairly well except he could never face a good roast dinner from the time he arrived until the day he left. Yet, if we had chips or custard the little boy would ask if he could finish the dish. Another must for him was the Royal Marine's Monday night film which commenced at six o'clock after which time no-one was allowed in. He became distraught if he missed it, and it was the only time I knew him to cry. His school was evacuated to join the Thurlestone school and his sister was billeted on an adjoining farm.

To illustrate the Royal Marine's training over our area I record one memorable example. One April evening I set out to walk up across our fields to the adjoining Hill Top Copse where we had some ewes lambing. Going through a gate to cross Hill Top Lane, suddenly, frightening me out of my wits, there was a mighty rushing sound and an explosion above my head. I had set off a trip wire and a rocket flare. Twenty yards on I set off another with no idea what they were for. Entering the sheep field there came from the copse voices yelling and swearing. 'What the bloody hell do you think you are doing?' I turned and walked towards them. 'You bloody fool you'll get shot!' I carried on to meet some cursing and camouflaged faces peering through the bushes. 'Who's in charge here?' I asked. After some discussion between themselves one Royal Marine claimed to be. 'Well I think I have as much right as you here. This is my farm and my lambing ewes and you could be liable for damages'. Their bombastic approach immediately calmed to friendliness. I did not think they could use live ammunition in a situation where there would be civilians at risk. The sheep had retreated to the top of the field and were none the worse.

I set off down across the fields again for home and after half way a hand suddenly grabbed my shoulder from behind. I turned to find two camouflaged marines had silently crept up on me. 'What do you think you are up to?' I asked. There was no reply as they held onto me. I explained who I was and eventually one said, 'We have to make sure you are not dressed up as a spy. If we cadets make a mistake we could lose our commission'. I assured them and they let me go.

Mentioning this in the sergeant's mess one evening later a sergeant coolly remarked to me 'Yes, that exercise was to take place in darkness with an 'enemy force' landing at Bantham to invade the valley. They were to be ambushed by the group at Hill Top Copse. The signal to start the exercise was to be a rocket flare, you set it off an hour early!'.

We became accustomed to these occasional accostings, but not so easily at night. 'Halt, who goes there?' 'Friend!' Now seeing the rifle pointing at you. 'Advance friend, and be recognised!' There was uncertainty who was on the end of it.

Another little incident happened one day when one of our boys was drawing turnips through muddy Hill Top Lane with our old horse Duke pulling the cart. He came running to find me and shouted 'Duke has dropped dead,' and then as if wanting an excuse from blame added, 'they there marines fired a gun!' I didn't know if that was true or not. I had seen Royal Marines crossing the fields but I had heard nothing. I was not surprised at Duke's death. He had worked so hard, willingly and willfully and probably died of a strained heart. I didn't know how father would take it, in bed from his second operation. Duke was one of his prime breeding. He took it calmly, after all he had seen many horses come and go. I took

Lion, Duke's life-long working mate, and with a chain around the dead horse's neck dragged him to the end of the lane for the knacker lorry to collect.

The Royal Marines Officer Cadet training was tough. They were put through it unmercifully by sergeants and corporals. New arrivals at Kingsbridge Station looked for the bus to take them out to Thurlestone. 'Bus – you bloody-well walk. Form up here'.

After exercising on Dartmoor, crawling around bogs for a day and a night, they marched twelve to fifteen miles back to barracks to their beds exhausted. Even then some preferred to clean their boots first rather than in the morning. Just asleep half an hour later, purposely, the alarm would sound. 'All hands on deck!'

The passing out parades were carried out with full military pomp, flags flying, and Plymouth Division Royal Marine band playing stirring marches, the strains of which cheered up the whole parish, wafting across on our westerly breezes. They took place on the commandeered playing field, unless wet, and then the large hotel garage was used as the barrack's square.

During the war working willingly to the cause was very evident. As well as the call up to the forces there were workers directed to essential industries and many volunteers offered help where they could. With so much shipping being sunk by German U-boats farming became more important. The attitude pre-war was not always so willing a one. The late 1930s brought better wages and conditions and a little more freedom. The young let it be known that they were not going to be so obligated to the long hours of work as their parents. They insisted on holidays and more recreation. They passed the harvest field gate, dressed for leisure, stating that they didn't care to help.

Now it was different again, food production essential. Varied were the workers offering help. But, how ever willing, some volunteers, because of not knowing the work, gave us problems. We forgave and got on with it.

The Women's Land Army was formed and given basic training. We received a letter asking us to try them. As father was ill I had to test them for our work and report back to him. We finally accepted a strong blonde girl. Our horseman remarked to me, 'You aren't going to let this one go?'. She stayed until the end of the war eventually marrying a Royal Marines sergeant.

Gangs of Women's Land Army girls could be hired for special jobs like threshing or potato work. The Thurlestone Royal Marines also allowed members of their demonstration squad to help. Some were old timers from north Devon who had been brought up on farms, and very useful. Italian and German prisoners of war were also available. The less said about the Italians the better, always grumbling and demanding food. The Germans were better, disciplined, fit and willing to work to end the war and get home. Fed up with Hitler I gathered. One retired farmer recently told me that he was not so lucky, a very pro-nazi prisoner chased him with a pitch fork threatening to kill him. That one was taken away for good.

We had three regularly on the farm for sometime with no trouble. They received one shilling a day above their normal allowance but it caused problems with our own troops who received less extra than the enemy they were fighting. The Royal Marines stopped helping.

Above Salcombe on the cliff top near Bolt Head an emergency airfield was hurriedly built because we were losing so many planes limping back across the Channel, damaged after action and needing a forward landing field. A full compliment of R.A.F. personnel lived in Nissen huts and the W.A.A.F. took over a Hope Cove hotel.

During the phoney war period of 1939 and uncertainty, a hush-hush message came to me that there was fear the enemy might land troops in gliders on our open spaces. Would I help dig in tall posts to wreck such an attempt at Bolt Head? Over two or three Sunday afternoons we completed the job. We were paid sixpence per afternoon, enough to buy a half pint of beer and a box of matches. Our posts had to be removed to make way for the airfield. After the war I saw similar posts on Dartmoor which remained until they rotted. The last to do so was reported in the press.

Through a friend I learned that every other Sunday evening a dance was held at the airfield in a Nissen hut, and a truck was sent to Hope Cove for the W.A.A.F.s. Any civilians wishing to attend would also be picked up at 6 o'clock. Dancing in war time started early and finished at midnight. Six o'clock was early for me. I had to finish milking, change and get to Hope Cove in time. But, telling no one, I took my sister's bicycle and dashed around the cliff path, sometimes catching the truck.

Should you think our lives were all work and dancing, they were, with popular songs like 'Roll Out the Barrel'. The beer flowed fast and fresh. So fresh that one night the heat of the room caused a hardly fermented barrel to blow out drenching the crowd amidst screams. But who cared, the music played on, and there maybe deaths tomorrow. These dances helped keep up morale despite the news of casualties. Loss of mates was not talked of easily. Apart from the sadness there were war slogans wisely observed – 'Mum's the word' and 'Careless talk costs lives'. Someone may whisper a little news or even tell you to keep quiet. It was surprising how little we knew of what was going on round about compared with present times when everybody expects to be told all.

BOMBING

The great fear of bombing in the cities at the start of the war was not quite as evident in the country areas. Our local air cover was the odd Wellington bomber, or the like, that flew over, and two Hurricane fighters on sorties now and again.

They usually appeared about fifteen minutes after the warning siren sounded. On the ground, we had practiced a little fire drill in our uncertainty but nothing for real.

One morning while thatching a hayrick up the top of the farm I heard two explosions and looking towards the sound saw two plumes of smoke rising over Salcombe. There was the sound of a plane racing away. It was one of the first tip and run raids after Dunkirk from occupied France. Two bombs destroyed a blacksmith's forge and a shop on the hill below Salcombe church. Just below that my uncle and aunt who had a grocer's shop were shaken but undamaged. Two hundred yards away my oldest sister and husband had a farm. War was coming home to us for the first time.

One Saturday mid-day I had just left Kingsbridge and reached West Alvington when I heard some terrific explosions. Turning round I saw smoke rising from Kingsbridge, a tip and run raid, the first of two on the town, and decided to turn back and help. After parking my car on the deserted quay I made for the bottom end of Fore Street and for the first time met bomb devastation. The street was full of debris, rubble, slates, splintered wood and glass. Where were the people? I saw none. I had in-laws there, proprietors of a book and paper shop. Picking my way through the debris I entered their unrecognisable, devasted shop and called upstairs to their flat. After what seemed a long pause came a feeble noise. I found them, man and wife, dazed and bewildered in the midst of their ruined kitchen. They could not speak. The bomb had been a direct hit on the shop behind theirs, killing the jeweller and his wife, both of whom I knew. The blast from that had splintered the window into needles of glass which had shot across the room like darts sticking into everything, even into the opposite wall. I knew I couldn't cope and went to look for help. In Fore Street I found a gang of men practiced for air raids, help was at hand. I went home feeling unprepared and useless.

Another afternoon whilst working in the garden I heard the drone of many planes. Looking through a thin veil of cloud I saw ghost like shapes of angular winged bombers, suspected enemy. Wave after wave and very high flying north. The quantity of awesome power overhead gave me a queer feeling. That afternoon they bombed Cardiff docks.

About seven o'clock one morning I was delivering milk to Bantham when I heard speeding planes and explosions. I looked to see smoke rising from Burgh Island Hotel. A tip and run raid had first bombed Aveton Gifford, demolishing the church and other property, then following down the River Avon to the sea deposited two surplus bombs.

The bombing of Plymouth was on a much larger scale. One evening at Thurlestone I joined a crowd gathered under the wall of a field, Ball Park, from which point we watched the destruction of Plymouth some fifteen miles distant. For us, stood in the dark it was the greatest fire-work display ever witnessed, for Plymothians horrifying. Explosions, criss-crossing searchlights, tracer bullets, sparkling magnesium incendiary bombs, flames and flashes and diving planes on fire.

The noise of battle was deafening. The heavy laden bombers came in over us distinctive by their labouring diesel engines with surges of power sounding like a speeded up version of an idling London bus. They dropped their loads and headed at speed towards the sea to escape. Another night they were deceived by decoy lights on Stoke Point and their dropped incendiary bombs burnt out twinkling like a million stars, an amazing sight.

With our inadequate defence Plymouth wasn't helped by Lord Haw Haw timely announcing each visit. The Plymouth bombing was almost equal to that of Coventry.

On one of these nights we were alarmed by a screaming bomb obviously falling very close. The explosion came, I believed on our cliffs, although some thought that it fell in Leasfoot Marsh. A large chunk of cliff that I knew well had disappeared, bombed or fallen naturally. Just watching had pricked my conscience and I went to Plymouth next morning to volunteer help. The same street chaos as at Kingsbridge but on a much larger scale. Their organised gangs wouldn't accept uninsured outside help. By mid-afternoon I had witnessed another unforgetable sight, a stream of Plymouth motor vehicles nose to tail trailing out to spend the night on Dartmoor overloaded with bedding, like a travelling caravan.

Another time a string of four small bombs fell in our parish across the fields behind Clanacombe House. I went to see the craters, not knowing then that after the war I would be farming that land with the craters filled in. Nowhere was completely safe. From the top of our farm we heard and saw aerial battles over the sea and distant fights against the U-boats. Diving and twisting wings flashed in the sunlight. Trails of smoke from damaged planes dived straight into the sea with the resultant splash.

JUNE DIARY
The cuckoo alters his tune.

Springing May is often considered best month of the year, but fulsome June is a rightful rival, the month of fastest growth.

Main crops remaining to be sown are kale, turnips and swedes, and earlyJune is not too late for mangels.

These root crops grown for winter fodder, were usually sown with a three row horse drill. Traditionally swedes were sown on mid-summer day or as near as possible. All later sown crops yield less.

Hay-grass cut before mid-summer and harvested well is better quality than later. 'Make hay while the sun shines', but sun cannot be commanded. Silage making, the alternative, also needs good weather for quality.

Special crop early potatoes if not marketed by second week in June can expect lower prices in the usual glut.

The mangels sown in May are horse hoed, between the rows as soon as the seedlings appear in rows before hand hoeing starts. A three row horse hoe is designed to follow the three row drill.

Hand hoeing and singling of mangel seedlings can begin at the four leaf stage. That is hoeing out weeds in the rows and at the same time leaving the single plants about one foot apart.

Sheep shearing season.

Fattened lambs marketed away from the ewes.

Fast growing high quality grass of May and June boosts flesh and milk production. The change from growth to ripening, noticeable after mid-summer, the dairy farmer especially will see a drop in milk yield after the spring flush! Another contributing factor to the reduced yield are the many fly pests that will irritate animals mercilessly for the rest of the summer.

Weeds cut in June will grow again soon.

Haysweep method

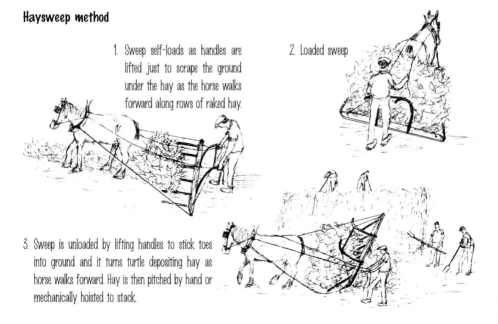

1. Sweep self-loads as handles are lifted just to scrape the ground under the hay as the horse walks forward along rows of raked hay.

2. Loaded sweep

3. Sweep is unloaded by lifting handles to stick toes into ground and it turns turtle depositing hay as horse walks forward. Hay is then pitched by hand or mechanically hoisted to stack.

JUNE

Summer's tenuous arrival needs fetes in May
But fulsome June bursts in her own assertive way
Conscious that all nature awaits welcomingly
To celebrate the long warm days and short nights madly.

Now that sun gods fiery orb is at zenith's peak
Live creation feeds on the nourishment it seeks
For growth, to flower, fruit and ripen maturely,
Among the leafy green abundance wholesomely.

There's awareness that seeding completes Nature's call
Mid-summer scents mown hay grass, the first to fall,
Other harvests are wont follow as gods of sun
Slowly turn down the heat, their Northern purpose run.

*Author testing hay
bales after rain.*

Looking up the valley towards Langmans hill top wood

Looking down the valley towards West Buckland and the sea.

CHAPTER 12
WAR AND FARMING FROM 1943

When the recruiting officer visited our farm he told me I should have to join an auxiliary service. I joined the Auxiliary Fire Service, later the National Fire Service, as one of the drivers in Thurlestone. We were loaned a garage and given a towing vehicle and an engine powered trailer pump. We slept there in pairs every sixth night and kept in touch by telephone with the head station at Kingsbridge. I couldn't sleep much there and went home tired at 6a.m. straight to the cows. We trained Sunday mornings and attended Kingsbridge for lectures and socials.

At the height of the war in those mad days we were young, worked hard and played hard. We spent too much time at night in our two pubs and tried not to miss a dance. Father warned 'You are getting to like beer too much'. He was right but I just managed to keep it under control.

The startling course of the war is well documented, we heard it direct on the radio and read newspapers. The farm was at full capacity when father was taken ill and needed a second operation. One of my busy days progressed as follows. I rose at 6a.m. – still dark because of the double summer time and first gave the cows a feed of hay before walking to the top of the farm to see the sheep some of whom were yet to lamb. Daylight would be breaking. I'd get back to the yard an hour later having checked one lot of bullocks on my way back. The staff had just arrived and would be milking the cows and seeing to other stock. I'd help them complete this work and then delegate the day's work. Then I'd go to the dairy to help the filling of the milk bottles, snatch a bit of breakfast and set off with the car on the milk round. I was the only available driver at the time. With double summer time many people didn't rise that early and didn't want their milk early.

I finished the milk round about 11a.m., then took the tractor to a field where volunteers were bagging seed potatoes from a clamp. They didn't wish to stop for lunch, nor did I. We were then to plant the potatoes. They took baskets full and set them in the furrows and I ploughed them in. At four o'clock they would leave. There was still one field of late corn to be drilled. It was a Saturday. A two man job usually, but I would have to manage alone. The corn drill was in the field, I had to drive home for the seed corn. Some of the staff were delegated to milk the cows and clear up the yard work that evening. I drilled the field quicker than expected, still with daylight and decided to harrow over the field to the usual good finish. As darkness approached I dashed across the two fields to check the lambing ewes again. Returning to the tractor and driving out of the gate onto the road I met our morning volunteers about 11p.m. They were walking back the two miles from the Churchstow pub, where they had spent the evening. Surprised, they remarked 'What, you're never still here?' After the morning work I had sat on the tractor for nearly twelve hours with still the sheep to see to again. There could have been a difficult lambing case to cope with, or a cow calving or other crisis. Fortunately there wasn't, but farming teaches that nature doesn't work to fixed hours. However tired you may be you have to be prepared to go again to the need. I've told many, though we were not in the trenches, it wasn't only those in uniform fought for Britain.

Weather wise 1943 was the wettest and dullest summer that I can recall, harvesting corn was very difficult with low yields. We tried not to do general work on Sundays but it was a Sunday in November for the war effort that we saved the last barley. Otherwise the grass fields we ploughed in 1940 continued to yield tremendously well.

At the end of 1943 came the surprise order from the government that an area surrounding Torcross in south Devon was to be completely evacuated for troop training purposes. It was traumatic for the inhabitants concerned especially just before Christmas, some who had never left their homes before.

It became a no-go area with so much hush-hush it gave us an uneasiness. Obviously something important was to happen there. The Torcross beaches were used to prepare for the proposed landing of allied troops in France. We were involved indirectly during that training period in various ways.

The Americans, now in the war after the Pearl Harbour disaster, were very much involved. When we stood alone after Dunkirk Churchill asked for their help or we could lose the war. They refused, but were persuaded to send massive supplies on a Lease Lend agreement. Now their troops and armour were arriving. My father as a Special Constable was sent on point duty where Americans with masses of vehicles and equipment were crossing a main road into the Torcross area.

They used the by-roads quietly, mostly at night, leaving the main roads to normal traffic. Father came home with only one remark. He didn't understand why their vehicles had long pipes sticking up at the back. I twigged why, but mum was the word and I didn't even reply to him. They were raised extensions to exhaust pipes which kept them above the water when landing from boats. It intimated to me what would be happening on Torcross beaches and proved how a chance remark could convey information to an enemy.

For the massive task of hurriedly evacuating residents, goods and chattels from the Slapton and Torcross areas extra lorries and crews were needed, some from London. They were encamped nearby.

One day I was ploughing a field when my good neighbour Leslie Rogers came running down to me shouting that he had just seen a robbery. The London lorry drivers had just delivered a last load, before returning to the capital, for an evacuated farmer to his uncle's farm at Lower Aunemouth. They were seen to enter my field, round up some hens, kill them by bashing their heads against the houses, pinch the eggs from the nest boxes and run off to their lorries. No doubt extras to rationed food welcomed by their families. I phoned the police who visited the camp. They came back to me with all they could find. Some brown eggs with names written on them. My hens' eggs were white. The thieves had flown. That was that.

One evening during this period our fire service was to visit Dartmouth, near the harbour in an evacuated area. We were told to walk around and familiarise ourselves in an area where there were several large gasometer type tanks and speak to no-one. I had no idea what I was seeing or why. Years later after the war, I learned they were oil tanks and part of the Pluto pipeline to the harbour. In the event of an enemy landing they were to be set alight. What would have been our role in that event is unknown.

Working for Kingsbridge Council at that time was Peggy Willoughby. She was delegated to visit the re-housed evacuated Torcross people to see to their needs. As can be imagined their alternative accommodation in variable conditions didn't make them happy. When that work finished she joined the W.R.N.S. and was stationed at Somerton, in Somerset.

The American forces were arriving in our area thick and fast. The somewhat overbearing attitude of their culture and obvious extravagance compared to our plainer way of living hit us. Wearing expensive uniforms and driving round everywhere in Jeeps, gum chewing, cigar smoking, and outspoken, jarred a bit. But we needed their help. Yes, they were over here, overpaid, and oversexed. We lived through it and with it. A contingent took over our other big hotel, The Links, at Thurlestone. I found them noncommittal in conversation, single minded towards ending the war, and in between searching for women and whisky. Partly because of their demand much of the whiskey allotted to pubs went 'under the counter' and was only brought out at a price.

One Saturday night before a dance at Kingsbridge some Americans entered a pub and after demanding whisky one asked loudly 'Where are the dames?' I couldn't help but say to one 'We don't like that attitude with your luxury stealing our girls'. Many girls, not all, enjoyed the luxury lavished on them. At dances the local lads were sometimes left with second choice, but I suppose all is fair in love and war.

An old timer lived next door to another pub I knew and he bought a few bottles of whisky when available, and when Americans were told there was none he would nudge them and say 'I'll get you a bottle'. He had halved the ones bought, filled them with water and so exploited the situation.

The Americans ate a lot of turkey, unheard of in our food rationed Britain. From one of their camps bins of giblets were taken to a dump where poor families waited and salvaged them to make delicious giblet pies.

Fully equipped and trained American forces were gathering all around us, spread out for safety, but converging on Torcross for embarkation, although we did not know that at the time.

Early one morning during May I was about to cross our farmyard, only half awake, and walked into a wire across my throat. Looking up I saw that several coloured wires crossed the yard into our orchard. They were insulated telephone wires put up during the night. The same mid-morning I had to drive to Churchstow and in the prolific hedgerow growth of late May groups of heavily armed and helmeted men were hiding. I was accosted by these serious looking troops before they lifted the wires to allow me past.

That Saturday evening in a Thurlestone pub before a local dance a group of grim faced American soldiers entered in full battle dress, dripping with weapons, and demanded whisky. The bar went quiet, a little apprehensive. These were desperate men before a battle they knew was coming. One of my sisters was present. She came to me and said 'These men are after me!' I replied 'You sit on my knee and say you are my wife'. Even so one came over and asked me 'How much for your wife for the night?' To our relief they soon left.

The one truth is that with the driving forces of nature being what they are there were surprise babies born. Under the circumstances no blame is attached or intended. The following incident reveals how laid back a country village like Thurlestone was then. Another of my sisters was doing our milk round at the time and called at a house where a baby was recently born. One morning with the pram in the garden she asked if she could see the baby. She visibly drew back in horror. The baby was black, the mother white.

A coloured person was seldom seen pre-war in Thurlestone, leave alone a baby. Today the mixed racial question is well aired along with many other once taboo issues. The war brought many coloured races here as well as Americans.

June 6th 1944 – it was announced that Allied forces had landed on the Normandy beaches. That site east of the Cherbourg peninsular was chosen on the chance that it would be sheltered from the prevailing south west wind. It wasn't, a south east wind blew for days and nearly wrecked the Mulberry harbour construction.

That wind also blew across the Channel towards south Devon. At the time I heard a continuous low sound like the rumbling of very distant thunder. I asked others if they heard it. It was the incessant thunder of guns and bombs as the Allies battled in France. The formidable opposition expected gave us an uneasy feeling at the height of the war as to which way it would end. The heroic fighting of the Russians on the Eastern Front, and determined British, American and Allies on the Western Front gradually squeezed Hitler to oblivion.

Stationed at the hotel in Thurlestone was a W.R.N.S. girl working with the Royal Marines. Her father was Commanding Officer at Somerton and she wished to be with him. By a stroke of luck Peggy Willoughby was able to swap with her. Peggy learned that she could ask to be billeted at home. This she did and walked into duty every day at Thurlestone Hotel passing through West Buckland en route. We often met and socialised at the Royal Marine dances becoming better acquainted than previously. She had not forgotten the young man she had met in the lane and we became friendly, a positive, helpful girl so different from the negative attitude I received at home. Eventually we were to marry but that was ten years later.

In August 1944 two enormous floating pontoons were washed up on our coastline. One at Bantham sands the other on rocks under the cliffs. They were each the size of a tennis court, constructed of large steel tanks and welded or bolted to huge iron girders. Further to that the tops were linked with wire hawsers, pulleys and winches. A mystery at the time, but later we learned that they were sections of the Mulberry D-Day harbour, that had broken free in a storm whilst being towed!

Royal Naval men appeared to anchor the monster on the sands before a favourable high tide would allow it to be towed off. To see how they anchored it securely on soft sand was a lesson in expertise. The importance of that section of Mulberry Harbour was revealed one day while we were harvesting corn. I was driving the tractor and a trailer load of sheaf corn up the hill from Bantham when a huge chauffeur driven American limousine met us. There wasn't room to pass. The limousine pulled up slowly in the middle of the road smoothly bouncing up and down as if on gossamer springs. Displayed on the bonnet was an American pennant flag. Inside was a heavily braided American naval officer intending to see for himself the pontoon situation. We sat looking at each other, I could not see to reverse with overhanging sheaves and the law was to give way to trailers. Eventually the Americans reversed with indignant looks on their faces to a wide enough passing place. Telling of this incident is of more importance because on top of my load was one of our three German POWs. He was a jovial young man who, after the car passed, smiled down to me, wagged a finger and shook his head. I nodded back to him and drove on. Here, at the height of the war, we two supposed enemies, one a captured beaten German, had humour enough to share it. With no words passed it said to me that war, power, and high rank, the world over, goes against the grain of ordinary working people.

The pontoon was soon towed away, the one on the rocks broke up. I retrieved a few shackles and wire ropes from it, hardly worth the exertion of carrying it up the cliff.

CHAPTER 13
SOAP

Thurlestone parish has a rugged coastline with five beaches and faces the south west prevailing weather. Through history 'wrecking', a local term now used for beach-combing, has been part of our living there.

One evening during February 1945 I happened to be in Thurlestone village for petrol when a relative coming home from work near the golf club told me that boxes of something were washing in on the high tide. Other men mentioned soap and tins of meat. My 'wrecking' instincts immediately triggered and I dashed off in the car to Bantham beach.

In the dim twilight I saw another in-law relative pulling boxes out of the water. A box washed in near me which I quickly carried up and hid in the rushes. That was mine whatever was in it. Then after pulling out more boxes we met. 'What are you going to do with them?' I asked. He said he didn't know. 'Well, they are of value and the Customs will have to know. Meanwhile you have no means of transporting them to safety. If you like I'll bring down a horse and cart after our milk round tomorrow, and we'll go fifty-fifty'. He agreed. The wooden boxes contained either tinned sausages or cakes of Sunlight soap. Each box weighed about 20 pounds. By next morning news had spread far, and with the tide half out when I arrived a beach full of people were following the tide back hoping to pull out more boxes. I carted away several boxes to the village and locked them in a shed.

That evening I visited Peggy Willoughby, my wife to be, in Bantham. I left her about 11o'clock and near the beach, my 'wrecking' bug struck again. It would be nearing low tide and I decided to walk down and see what it had left. The moon was full in a clear sky. Alone, I witnessed an amazing sight. The whole expanse of Bantham Sands right out to low-tide was littered with cakes of Sunlight soap evenly distributed by the slow action of a quiet ebbing tide. They shone bright in the moonlight against the wet sand. I could hardly walk between them. The wooden boxes had broken apart.

Next morning it was fine and mild again when the high tide would cover the soap. I told our man and two boys after milking to take the tractor and trailer and potato baskets to the beach and pick up the loose cakes of soap. I had the milk round to do as father was in bed again with muscular trouble, his legs had given out.

Crowds were on the beach expecting boxes to be washed in. They hadn't a receptacle between them. Amusingly they stuffed cakes of soap anywhere in their clothing that would hold it. Some ran home for baskets. One farmer sent home for his tractor and baskets. We filled our trailer and from memory I seem to remember twenty-two boxes and twenty-two hundredweight of loose soap was collected.

The day after the soap the broken box-wood also washed in. We filled a trailer with that and by lunch time in beautiful warm sunshine for February sat in our shirt sleeves on the rocks at low tide and ate a lunch of pasties made from the tinned sausages that my mother had baked and brought to us by George our evacuee boy. Peggy Willoughby also joined us.

The soap had come from an American supply boat 'Persier' torpedoed near the Eddystone light. Among the cargo was over 2,000 tons of soap. One of the other rationed items that was washed up was eggs in dried powder form, but horrible to taste if a packet could be found that sea water had not entered.

The Customs officer warned salvagers that they should declare their 'booty' on the forms he provided. Later he called house to house and many were fined for not reporting their good fortune. But much had travelled miles away and was well hidden. The officer who came with my form kindly said 'See you keep enough for yourself', which I did by hiding a couple of boxes under straw bales in a shed, but to my chagrin some time later, found that rats liked to eat it and had almost cleared the lot. With the load of box-wood we made chitting trays for sprouting early potatoes. We were paid for the soap that the Customs retrieved from us, making the salvage worthwhile.

PULLING TOGETHER

At the height of the war there was still uncertainty which way it would end and that affected our thoughts and feelings, although Churchill would not allow us to consider defeat by constantly plying with his courageous oratory. I feel that I have not emphasised sufficiently the degree of pulling together to the necessisty in the total war. The atmosphere of a once large clear world now appeared thickened and hung on our conciousness as if we were trapped in a very small world-like fish bowl with a killer predator at large. There was no escape, we had to face it and live or die in the attempt. That realisation brought us together, to accept the dictates of leaders and warlords without question, however irksome it was to stick it out, uncomplaining and cheerfully to keep up morale.

Death was constantly at hand, emphasising how being alive was so precious and why we lived to capacity in work and free time. No longer, as pre war, could you choose a career and further it to your own ends. Unless that work were of use to the war effort you were soon trained to another need. I soon learned that our farm was part of the war effort, no longer our own choice of work but producing to government demand and we could be disposessed if failing. It was not easy and some farmers were replaced by the War Agricultural Committee.

My attempt has been to show how involved we were with the whole effort and less of self interest, and why I have written of events outside farming that seriously affected our outlook as we lived through them. From Dunkirk onwards our emotions, always with war in the background, wavered towards depression or elation with each battle lost or won.

A DUNKIRK STORY

Mentioning the heroic retreat from Dunkirk, which has just celebrated its sixtieth and final anniversary, reminds me of a remarkable exploit with local consequences. During one of the recent television sixtieth anniversary of Dunkirk programmes an officer involved in the little ships rescue stated that it would not have been successful if the English Channel had not been flat calm and misty for two whole days and nights. These ideal weather conditions allowed the following story to take place. Everyone who lived through the war has a story. Here is an extraordinary one of the many. A Kingsbridge farmer and schoolboy contemporary with me told it and confirmed it recently. Some years after the war had finished he and a farmer friend decided to go to a sheep sale in the north of England where, as potential bidders, they were obliged to register their names and addresses with the auctioneers. On hearing the town of Kingsbridge mentioned one of the auctioneers remarked 'Kingsbridge in Devon, I know that place, come into my office after the sale and I will tell you a war story'.

With the sale duly completed the two farmers called in the office and over a glass of whisky the auctioneer began his story.

'I was at the retreat towards Dunkirk, when the order came 'Every man for himself, make for the beaches where with luck a boat will pick you up'. We were four officers sticking together. Going down a small creek in a village we saw on a bank a small row boat with oars. Without question or stopping we dragged it to the water and rowed away as fast as we could to get out of the range of gunfire from the shore. We could see and hear at some distance the battle over Dunkirk. We were at the west and kept rowing north hoping a boat would pick us up, but the tide was carrying us west away from the ships. We didn't want to land back in France so kept rowing for England, hopefully. We saw nothing and rowed on into the night. Tired we ate our little food and just kept going all next day not knowing where we were in the mist. As it slowly cleared we saw land and white houses along a cliff top. They weren't French, looked English. Rowing towards them we realised we were entering the mouth of a small river and decided there would be habitation there where we could land. The tide carried us round a bend and we saw a few boathouses with cottages above them. We saw no-one and no-one accosted us. We decided that it was too small a place for our needs and rowed on up river. At about seven in the morning we came to a road bridge across the river and we landed there. Tired and disheveled we staggered up to the road and saw a postman cycling sleepily towards us. He blinked in disbelief and nearly wobbled off his bike. 'Where is this place?' we asked. Suspicious that we were the enemy he was reluctant to answer. We explained who we were and eventually he told us it was Aveton Gifford on the River Avon. (Here I should explain their first sighting of land was Bigbury Bay, which is 300 miles from Dunkirk. It was remarkable that they were not picked up nor were spotted by our coastal watch.) 'Where's the nearest police station?' we next asked the postman, because our instructions in such circumstances were to report to the nearest. 'There is a policeman lives in the village just up the road'. We made our way there to more suspicion and disbelief. After several phone calls the policeman allowed us in. His wife cooked us a good breakfast, after which I as senior officer, formed up the men and marched up a very steep hill on route for Kingsbridge Police Station. That's how I came to know Kingsbridge'.

Should this story of their journey seem improbable remember these were desperate men trying to save their lives. Apart from their luck in having ideal weather conditions no northcountryman could have described the unusual route from Bigbury Bay to Kingsbridge, via the River Avon and Aveton Gifford, so accurately without having actually made it. Attempts to trace any of these men, if still alive, have to date proved unsuccessful.

CHAPTER 14
END OF THE WAR

The national day of celebration for victory in Europe was on 8th May 1945. In Thurlestone our celebrations were marred by the tragic accidental death of the Commander-in-Chief Royal Marines.

The marines were using live ammunition across a valley a day or two before VE Day whilst on exercise. The C. in C. sat in a vehicle with bullet proof side screens. To show bravado and encourage his men he commanded 'Come on let us drive through the firing'. The vehicle was open topped and driving across the steep valley side became exposed to the firing. He received a bullet through the head and died instantly. He was a popular officer and at our rejoicing a gloom was felt throughout the Royal Marine establishment. He was buried at Thurlestone church with full military honours at 10 a.m. on VE day, and instructions were that there should be no victory celebrations until after. The village respected that. It is ironic that Thurlestone witnessed an accidental death on the first day of war with a drowning at Bantham and buried the C. in C. on the last.

Then of course we celebrated, with a Church Service of thanks followed by singing, dancing and drinking in the streets. It finished in the Thurlestone Hotel ballroom at an hour few of us can remember.

But the war was not completely over, the horrible Japanese version still raged in the east. That was to end abruptly after the Americans dropped a second atom bomb, which had such devastating effect that the Japs surrendered unconditionally, no doubt saving lives in an otherwise long drawn out war. The celebration of Victory in Japan, VJ Day, took place on August 15th 1945.

We farmers were asked to carry on harvesting through the day and celebrate at night because shortages were worse at the end of the war than through it, part of the price we paid. We were cutting a very fine field of oats, standing as high as the tractor and a photograph was taken of it, but I can't locate it now. Our farm, like most, was still producing very fine crops as every acre did throughout the war. Looking back on it now is to remember the achievement and satisfaction in seeing our soil in full production to the need. I was proud of our war effort, despite the long hours, sweat and backache, it mattered not. We won through was what mattered. I was lucky to have lived at home through it, and ever conscious of the upsetting sacrifices others had made.

The war was over, but at what terrific cost of lives and materials. There was relief to the mind, a lifting of the weight of blackness that had lurked there, but a weight of sadness remained to mourn for so many lost of our generation. I remember it after the first war, although very young, for years the quitness of a

Clanacombe farmhouse.

The view from above Clanacombe House across to Langmans fields and West Buckland village.

shocked nation, but it was not as severe this time in the more technical war.

Through those technical advances Britain could never be the same again, or intended to be. So many things had changed. The troops came home with a determined spirit, not to be forgotten as many were after the first war. They insisted on making 'a country fit for heroes to live in'.

With shortages and rationing continuing for many years our farming carried on much the same, now with our local labour again. Volunteers, POWs, landgirls, troops, evacuees, all went their ways. The Royal Marines left Thurlestone Hotel during April 1946.

In that year another offer to rent a farm came to me. Clanacombe Farm owned by Mr. Lothian-Mathews of Clanacombe House had become vacant. The land was adjoining Langmans to the south east extending up the valley, and just under fifty acres. It was small enough and steep ground, but I knew there was a living there. I would have preferred something less steep after years at Langmans, but officers were vacating the forces with large accrued sums of money and buying farms. I didn't miss the Clanacombe offer.

The farmhouse at Clanacombe was stone built as two semi-detached cottages with a communicating door between. It could be used as one farmhouse or two service cottages to the main house. One cottage was occupied by the gardener and family, the other by evacuees from Plymouth. I didn't need them, living at Langmans and being still single.

Father gave me a second-hand tractor, seven bullocks and £200 cash to set me off. That was my pay for twelve years work, extra to my keep at Langmans. Rising prices from the war had started a slow inflation. At the time the farming press had stated that it was impossible to start farming with less than £10,000 capital.

We ran two farms together for four years which was an advantage sharing labour and implements, but in 1950 with my father approaching sixty-five years of age, he decided he had had enough and intended to retire.

Our Langman's landlord had written to say he wished to sell the farm and the first offer was to my father the tenant. As sitting tenant he was advised to buy it. But he couldn't afford to, and at his age the bank wouldn't lend him the money. It was then suggested he borrowed the money in my name, but the bank wouldn't loan the extra capital for me to farm it. Father was right in thinking I could not farm two steep farms without sufficient capital and pay off a mortgage. Langmans Farm would have to be sold with vacant possession. The farm cottage would be retained in my parents' ownership where they would retire. It was a bitter blow to give up a good home of thirty-one years, but the profit from the sale gave me sufficient capital to establish Clanacombe Farm.

Many tenant farming families of long standing were caught in the same way. With land prices rising fast after the war, owners wished to cash in and wouldn't pass leases on to the families' younger generation. So serious was the loss of experienced young farmers that the law was changed in their favour. It came too late for me, I was one of the victims.

The years of toil and his operations through the war years had taken their toll on my father. He told no-one but his doctor that he had a heart problem and died suddenly in 1953. After his death my mother's first words to me were 'That man has worked hard'. Other tributes that followed included 'He was a man with a purpose, who kept his troubles to himself', 'An honest man, straight and reliable, the district will be missing him'. One old neighbouring farmer who, after the war saw 'new' farmers come and go, was heard to say 'Farmer Snowdon would grow more corn in one field than they could grow on their whole farm'.

Why Thurlestone did not suffer too much in the 1930's depression was mentioned in Chapter One. It possessed two class hotels and the golf links, all with exceptional scenic views over the bay that attracted first class visitors in increasing numbers. The motor car brought the wealthy and there were professional and business people doing well enough despite the depression who drove from Plymouth, Kingsbridge, or wherever, played a round of golf and drove home again. Some decided to build fine houses beside the golf course. This provided work for the village families, building, landscaping gardens, stone walling and hedging etc. The hotels and some large houses also required domestic staff.

Many ageing farm workers took on this work to which they were well suited, but were lost to the farms. The most industrious and thrifty of these were able to leave their village cottages and build new homes in the 1930's ribbon development above the village. A detached three bedroomed house and garden cost little moe than three hundred pounds and the owners took in bed and breakfast guests. That trade was expanding throughout the parish, which all helped Thurlestone through the depression.

My life farming at Clanacombe from 1946 will make another story. I must add that I married Peggy Willoughby in 1955, an excellent partner, more so than I could have expected. When my landlord, Mr. Lothian-Mathews died, I was given the opportunity to buy the farm. For the second time I had the advantage of a sitting tenancy, again a chance not to be missed. From a very small boy my dream was to own a plot of land and live off it. I achieved that and within the law of the land did as I pleased with it.

I have described previously my integral man, a farmer, leader, reliable, and a tower of strength to society – and knew I had not that personality. He judges and delegates well. Although managing through the war with many willing helpers, I do not do that well, preferring to do everything myself and in my own way. Among the usual anxieties and trials of farming there were moments of complete fulfillment when standing amidst my own fields of crops and livestock at the head of the valley, and looking out towards Burgh Island and the sea beyond. Wondrously beautiful at times. It would have been folly to have chosen a different career and leave the valley I loved so much.

Poet Sa'di's words come back to me, after I farmed as well as able. 'Then you need not depend on any man'. This brought the word yeoman to mind. I checked in my encyclopedia – 'a countryman, a class of small freeholders intermediate between labourer and gentry'. Chambers dictionary – 'a farmer who owns and works his own land'. And that is how I wish to be remembered, as a yeoman of England.

Through delays it has taken two years to complete this book and while doing so farming has again gone into depression, seemingly to the extinction of some family farms. To my disgust the news becomes grimmer. Our country, one of the finest agricultural countries with temperate climate, and with the finest of farmers, is so badly considered.

Everyone eats to live and that food comes from the soil and the sea. Knowing that half the world's population is undernourished this present trend cannot be understood.

Those with the powers that control world affairs, be they scientific, technical, political or financial have made advances and progressed to our supposed betterment. But, invention for good always brings attendant evil with it. The price being paid for the profit is the upsetting of the balance of life forms on our planet. If the power-lords see light for the future it is beyond my ability to comment on that. And why at my age should I care for the future, except that I feel a moral duty to pass on to posterity useful experience from a lived life. Much of that I have recorded in the written form.

If the state of British farming was as bad as at present, when I was about to start to write this book, I doubt it would have been written, but as my disgust mounted at each unbelievable farming set-back so my determination mounted that the request should be fulfilled.

Whether the future world be a success or disaster, at least people will know there was a sustainable way of life before the great change and will or could have continued as long as our planet is destined to be green. There is the question of how much human population the world can support satisfactorily in balance with the other wonderful life forms designed to share our earth space. Why species are predatory on one another is an enigma. Possibly survival of the fittest is a necessity for the stamina required for successful life.

Sa'di's poem gives a formula for life that I agree with and states that we should make effort to pay back the debt we owe our country's soil.

That debt cannot be paid with man-made money, nature doesn't deal in it. A recent television programme on the history of money described how that soon after its inception there was advice on dangers of its use. It ended by stating it still exists because we like it and the amount we own is a measure of our status. I add that liking it is one thing, but loving it according to the bible is evil.

The value of man-made money cannot be fixed against nature. For ourselves, we can make it what we wish, hence inflation. We can pay each other with it, but not the debt we owe the Good Earth. That debt is to be paid by effort. Dare I say work? Effort is required to maintain the precious and delicate balance in Nature's scheme, to pass it on for the enjoyment of those to follow.

I confess that I know not what or who God is, but know of godliness. That is having lived close to nature, there is an awareness of an almighty power existing and I feel it not to be accidental.